THE BARGAIN HUNTER'S
ANTIQUES HANDBOOK

Phoebe Phillips was born in New York and came to England to study Shakespeare, where she has lived ever since. She has been an editor and writer for twenty-five years of illustrated books, especially on the arts and antiques, history and gardening. One of her books, *Complete Encyclopedia of Antiques*, is still in print after twenty-two years. Phoebe Phillips now divides her time between London and Suffolk, where she runs antiques stalls in three different markets.

Tom Robb travelled the fairs and trawled the markets taking pictures and making sketches for the illustrations. He lives in London, but wanders far afield painting, and antiquing on the way.

The Bargain Hunter's Antiques Book

The Insider's Guide to Antiques and Collectables Under £100

Phoebe Phillips

Drawings
Tom Robb

HEADLINE

First published in 1993
by HEADLINE BOOK PUBLISHING

First published in paperback in 1994
by HEADLINE BOOK PUBLISHING

10 9 8 7 6 5 4 3 2 1

ISBN 0 7472 4550 9

Printed and bound in Great Britain by
HarperCollins Manufacturing, Glasgow

HEADLINE BOOK PUBLISHING
A division of Hodder Headline PLC
338 Euston Road
London NW1 3BH

To the market traders of Suffolk, to the many dealers at Bermondsey and Portobello and Camden, to every market trader standing or sitting all day, getting up in the cold morning, giving up their weekends to pack up in the dawn and pack up again when the sun has gone, answering questions, cheering each other up, sharing the good days and the bad with each other, and always saying goodbye, see you next time, with a smile...
this book is dedicated.
All their help is gratefully acknowledged, the errors being ours alone.

Introduction

Collecting has become a national pastime as potent as the lure of buried treasure. Perhaps some of this new craze has been due to the enormous popularity of the various television shows and magazines, which have finally allowed us to see how much beauty and excitement there is in our everyday decorative crafts of only yesterday.

Today, too, we have finally recognised that the expert who refused to acknowledge any craft after 1850 was both foolish and mistaken. New styles are often suspect to the older generation, and once upon a time our now precious 18th century artifacts were sneered at by devotees of the 17th century!

There's also been a revival in home and interior design which has sparked off interest in acquiring just the right object for just the right space. This is a first fatal step - soon the well-dressed room gives way to a collection of even more wonderful objects, to become an Aladdin's cave of treasures instead.

Buying on a budget is not just a negative activity, based on how much you *cannot* spend, leaving you full of frustration and regret. Collecting carefully can increase your expertise and knowledge; not being able to afford to make mistakes is a great incentive to learn as much as possible about your subject.

Visiting museums and smaller auction rooms are still cheapest opportunities for study. You can see all sorts of details and textures that no photograph or drawing can possibly convey. Only that sort of experience will give you a little edge when you start bargain hunting in earnest.

When I did, so many years ago, I gladly admitted that collecting has a touch of natural greed. Buying something which is, or will be, worth more than we have to pay is bargain hunting, and I see no reason to be ashamed of it. Few of us today can afford to spend money regularly on extravagant purchases, guaranteed to be the best of their kind, unless it's for a very special occasion. When and if we do, we know that we are paying not just for the object itself, but for the expertise of the person who is selling it.

That should be the spur to acquire expertise and an eye of your own, to learn about some of the newer areas and unusual objects, and to open your eyes to the potential of previously neglected objects and periods which are becoming more and more interesting to the world of art and antiques. We can't promise you the find of the century every time, but we can promise you a lifetime of enjoyment looking for it.

We hope antiques will become for you, as it has been for us, bargain hunting of the most exciting kind! Here's to luck and treasures for all of us.

Phoebe Phillips
Tom Robb

Contents

How To Use This Book

Looking for antiques is a delightful but hectic pastime, so I've tried to make this book as easy to use as possible. The categories are based mainly on objects because in my experience that is what most people like to collect. We have also included major materials - brass, pottery, silver, etc.

There is an index for cross-reference, so that you can find additional types of objects, or more examples of individual designers.

Our drawings, even though there are over 500 of them, can only be single examples of what may well be a varied and fascinating group. So please use the text and the picture as starting points to get you going rather than the last word about an entire genre.

The left-hand column on each double page has a short introduction and "Collectors' Notes" for a brief history and some important technical information, while the remaining columns contain illustrations and captions about individual pieces, as well as additional notes about some of our dealers' experiences, triumphs and disasters. The Notes as well as the captions mention particular problems of fakery, repair and restoration relevant to that kind of object, and to that subject.

The reference sections at the end include a book list, arranged by subject. The list is a personal one, based on those volumes which, over the years, I have found interesting to read, or helpful about those areas and subjects which aren't generally covered. I'm sure there are some very good books which have been missed. If you have found a useful publication about your favourite subject, please let me know and we'll try to include it in the next edition.

There will naturally be some which will be currently out of print, but most of these should be available from a specialised dealer or a good second-hand shop.

We haven't been able to include every subject which is intriguing, new or collectable. Please write with suggestions.
PRICES
Our prices are based on sales made during the past few months at the markets and fairs I and some of my colleagues attend.

Most dealers do give an extra discount, between five to fifteen percent, to fellow dealers, and so we have added ten percent back where the price was a purchase or sale to another dealer. Naturally there will be other prices at other markets, but between us we more or less cover the country, and I have also included prices from Bermondsey, Camden and Portobello in London.

There is no guarantee that something we have sold or bought would be the same price in another market or even during another sale at the same place. That is true of even the most prestigious auction house, when you are dealing with individual items.

In considering what you have paid, condition is vital; don't be tempted to think that because we are dealing exclusively with prices under £100, cracks or missing bits won't affect the value. They will, they do.

Please also remember that prices can vary enormously across the country. An area rich in local pottery might price up copper or lacquer boxes; a town with a street of good antique shops will have more competitive prices than the lonely shop, which has no competition for miles, and charges accordingly.

When you buy from a dealer, the price can also vary because it is based on what was paid and how it was acquired. If something was bought cheaply, as part of a job lot, any reasonable dealer can afford to give you a good price in return. If they paid heavily because of its quality, they will be expecting a higher profit.

There are some dealers who are greedy just as there are some customers who haggle beyond endurance, but if both are reasonable then two contented people are the result.

When you begin to buy regularly, make a note of what you paid, when and where you bought it, and what might have affected the price, like condition or doubt about the mark. Keep this record safe for guidance as well as a reference to future investment.

Auctions, Fairs and Markets

AUCTION SALEROOMS

A lot of new collectors feel hesitant about bidding or even attending an auction, because there have been so many over-dramatic stories of what can happen on television or in newspapers. Don't be put off - there are a few simple rules of etiquette to follow, that's all.

Whenever you see the advertisement for an auction, no matter how small or how important, it gives the date of the sale, and the viewing dates.

Make a note to attend the viewing. This is absolutely vital. Even if they have a catalogue to buy, and many smaller auction houses have none, if you bid either without examining the object, or only on what you can see as the object is held up, you are taking a considerable risk which many experts would baulk at. If your time is really that limited, then go to the viewing and leave a bid with the auctioneer's clerk.

Most viewing days are just before the sale; go prepared with pen and paper. Give yourself enough time - I can't say that too strongly. Make one quick tour of the room, decide what you are really interested in, and then give those items a good deal of attention. This is opportunity time; look at the backs of chests, inside drawers, under chairs, and behind sofas. Delve deep into boxes of books or china ("assorted" can and does mean anything) and check out the inside cupboards of sideboards and desks. You can touch (albeit carefully!) and feel textures and stroke planks looking for concealed cracks or plastic fillers. Hold china to the light, tilting it back and forth so that any irregularity, yellowish repair area or chipped glazing will become apparent. Make notes of everything you find, and double check the numbers on those pieces you decide to bid on. In the heat of the moment, you may not even see the object held up for identification - sometimes the auctioneer simply waves in its general direction. Having careful notes should also keep you from becoming too excited and going beyond what you are really prepared to pay.

Talk to the porters - they are usually a mine of information. They will tell you what they think the piece will bring, they will tell you if there is a floor - i.e., a bid already registered with them, so that nothing underneath that amount will be considered. Most of all, they've had a chance to see your particular object for a few days, and probably others very like it over the past years. Listen to their advice. It's not always right, but it's always worth the trouble of a hearing.

If you want them to make a bid on your behalf, either because you can't attend or you're perhaps too nervous, you can fill out a form and leave it or stay to watch the fun.

Unless you are known to the auctioneer and have arranged it, you will have to pay almost immediately, and take away your prize as soon as possible. Ask before the auction about the house rules; each auction house has its own regulations.

Don't worry that scratching your nose or your head will be taken as a bid. Those tricks also have to be agreed ahead of time!

Become a regular visitor; auctions are like moving museums. Keep catalogues of those subjects which really interest you and ask for the price records afterwards. They form a record not only of prices but of what comes onto the market, in what condition, and how it is described.

Over the months and years, you will see such a wide variety of objects that your collector's education will benefit way beyond your expectations.

ANTIQUE FAIRS AND MARKETS

In the past, they appeared twice or three times a year in fashionable venues; now antique fairs are one of the success stories of the decade. No doubt this is due to the Antiques Roadshow with a little Lovejoy on the side, but whatever the reason, everyone has benefited. Dealers can come out to meet their public instead of waiting in shops, while the public can really enjoy the pleasures of table-shopping. You can pick things up, look at them closely, ask about price and background and condition, and even buy! All without being intimidated by plush surroundings or hushed voices. Yet this can be made even better with a little extra trouble.

Go with a notebook to take down names and addresses of dealers as well as notes of prices. If you are seriously interested in a subject, ask about it. We can't bring everything every week, but we will usually be able to bring something on spec.

Don't believe it when someone says that being denigrating or poker-faced will get you the best price. I can assure you that when everyone else seems to be on holiday, a few intelligent questions, a smile and some honest enthusiasm will make us much more inclined to take a reasonable offer than to bargain for the last penny.

Assume as much good faith in your dealer as you are prepared to bring to the transaction. Very few of us deliberately over-price or mis-describe our goods; it would be self-defeating. Nor do we operate, as some larger auction houses grandly assume, on a fly-by-night basis. I go to three different markets, and each has its dealers who come every week or month, seeing regular customers as well as new ones.

It does pay to ask if the price is negotiable - at the end of the day dealers packing up are sometimes willing to sell quickly rather than take a bulky object home again. And at an outside market a bad day and rainy weather can make a so-so offer tempting.

But moderation in all things. I have seen dealers turn down a sale over and over again when confronted with a buyer who tries to push a genuine offer down either by rubbishing the object or just being offensive. Negotiating is an option, and it's the owner's right, not the customer's. Having said that, the big weekly city markets may be a little less permanent. There are more temporary stalls with dealers who turn up only when they have somewhat dubious goods to sell, and are seldom careful about their facts when it comes to reproduction or outright fakes.

It takes two to make a bad bargain as much as a good one. Fulfil your own half of the deal by doing your research and reading up as much as you can on the subject in question.

Take the time and trouble to look around as we have suggested, and you'll be a lot less gullible and much more able to spot the poor copies without having to rely on the dealer. Keep an eye on prices so you'll have a good feeling for what is reasonable, because far too little is as dangerous as far too much. After all, if you do think you are getting away, not with a bargain but with a positive steal, then you have to assume that you as the buyer knows more than the seller. And if you fool yourself into believing that with no justification, then you are a party to the disappointment.

Most bad purchases, and I've made quite a few, are self-deception. You are either tired at the end of the day, and didn't know when to stop, or so pleased with your own cleverness at finding a special plate or a particular pattern that you don't stop to examine the base or look at the edges or check for traces of cracks and restoration.

Buyer Beware is an old saw, but Buyer Pay Attention is more truthful.

CAR BOOT SALES

Car boot sales are the latest phenomenon and so much a rag bag of left-over tat and genuine clearance items that you have to be both energetic and persevering to make any use of them.

Go on the aassumption that 99 percent of what you see will be awful. Then if you are lucky you'll find the one or two stalls which have something interesting or at least are potentially worth the effort.

This is a cash business. No chequebooks need be taken. And you have to get there early. By now, with the recession, the rise in general competition and the high costs at many auctions, dealers are finding it quite useful to attend one or two sales regularly, and they arrive as they open. Smaller boot sales for local charities are the best opportunity because they often include many discards from decent homes rather than supermarket rejects. They are also a good place to get rid of your own outgrown bargain collectables.

Animal Models

All the world loves a bunny rabbit...or a cat, or a teddy bear... the list is endless. Collecting animals can be a major source of pleasure for both buyer and seller.

Some collectors concentrate on one species, anything from turtles to tyrannosaurus rex in any form, paper, plastic or plate. Others collect all kinds of animals but only ceramics, or even more specialised, only a trademark like Wade or SylvaC. Those shown here are just a glimpse of the possibilities; see the index for additional animals included under other categories.

COLLECTORS' NOTES

While single examples can be quite remarkably valuable - like the famous Meissen figurines - at our bargain level having a focussed collection will repay you as an investment for the future. When and if you decide to sell, animal collectors, who are usually more emotional than most about their subject, will either buy the lot or come back time after time to add to their hoard.

Popular miniature pottery models are generally fairly young antiques and they need to be in the best condition. Many date from the 1930s to the 1950s and there is relatively little in general reference book material. On the other hand, attribution is less of a problem since most are clearly marked. Pay careful attention to sale prices and information about rarity. Talk to specialised dealers as often as you can because price guides can be very misleading, ranging from £25 to £50 for apparently similar pieces.

The market for other animal collectables varies even more; why should silver pig pincushions be more popular than other models? I've no idea, but they are. Cats sell to cat lovers who become cat collectors. Embroidered animals of any kind are rare and usually worth buying; sketchily painted, generalised animals and birds are quite common, but finely modelled big figurines are a decorator's dream, and even 1930s' examples can be worth many hundreds.

1. Lacquer box with brightly painted parrot; birds are often used in decorative pieces because of their colouring.

Most animals have their fans, but pigs, swans, horses, cows, cats and dogs seem to be the other most collectable themes. Little lacquer boxes have been hand-painted for decades in India, so they are very common, but like many tourist items, now rather grandly "memorabilia", the best ones are turning up in second-hand shops. Look for a good finish along the edges without chipped wood or paint, but with well-fitting lids and individual patterns. Try to find unusual subjects and shapes, which sell better than the standard all-over patterns.

Even new, they'll only be £4-7. An inexpensive and rewarding way to build a pleasant collection at little cost, and which can be easily displayed.

2. An obedient dog as coat hook, suitable for the gun room! Made in china and iron, c. 1880, it fulfilled the Victorian ideal of nature applied to useful work. Unmarked. £30-40.

3. In 1901, Shaw and Copestake founded a pottery in Staffordshire. From the 1930s to their closure in 1982, they produced inexpensive and attractive novelties. "SylvaC" was their trading name, impressed or printed. In recent years SylvaC has become highly collectable. Many of their wares used three-dimensional and appropriate patterns, like a celery vases moulded as a bunch of celery, but they are also known for little animal models. Some were ornamental, others were combined with function: a monkey vase, a rabbit money-box, or dog pin-tray.

Generally glazed in single colours, a few, like this terrier in brown and white, were painted in naturalistic combinations. SylvaC figures of the 1930s are more stylised than those made by Wade, their biggest rival. £25-45.

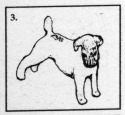

4. During the 20th century Japan became a leading exporter to Britain. Today their reputation of being only a nation of copiers has been challenged as we begin to appreciate the artistry and sense of humour in many of their ceramic wares. Designed unashamedly for the European market, at its best the modelling is amusing and the little pieces are often made of good porcelain. This pearl lustre and brightly painted duck lemon squeezer is one of the most delightful designs, and typical of the 1920s imports which are now being avidly collected, but only in perfect condition. I've also seen a pelican, too. Make sure the reamer matches the base. £28 if complete and unchipped, £12 for reamer alone.

5. An over-life-sized cat of many patterns and colours, its papier-mâché body somehow remaining unscathed in its long trip from Mexico sometime in the 1930s.

The large black eyes and the generous size (it's over 2 feet in length) give it enormous presence, the perfect fireplace feline. Papier-mâché animals are common in Mexico, made for celebrations and festivals, but old ones seldom turn up in Europe, and cats, which are so popular, are even rarer. Watch out for chips; this one is perfect. £70-80.

6. A tiny silver pig pincushion, hallmarked Birmingham 1933. The original thin blue velvet has been replaced with thicker brown cloth, reducing the value to £22-25.

15

Artists' Tools

Equipment for artists is one of those specialised subjects which nonetheless appeals to a surprisingly wide audience. Easels are easy to appreciate; many small table models are delightfully carved and useful today for photographs as well as paintings. Those wonderful wooden paint boxes have their own charm, especially when the label is still in place in all its baroque glory. Another more unusual find are old palettes with messy coats of dried paint and brushmarks; many collectors of modern art might find them attractive as "found" objects, to be hung on the wall like abstract paintings!

COLLECTORS' NOTES

Easels were made both for display and for real work. Display easels can date from the 18th century onwards; large models were used in fashionable artists' studios to show off the latest study or oil. Victorian examples were wonderfully elaborate; they are quite rare now and the full-size ones are beyond our limit, but small table models do appear from time to time, and are easier to fit into a modern home. Watch out for fakes carved abroad, or small metal versions cast recently from over-bright brass.

Boxes for oils and watercolours are always eagerly sought by artists looking for useful and unusual sizes. The quality of fine wood and the craftsmanship used in their manufacture are simply not available today. Even watercolour tinplate boxes were made by hand, while today's examples are mass-produced and pressed, or made of plastic.

The paints themselves are seldom usable, but they give a good indication of their age by the kind of tube, the names of the colours and the label design. Oil colours would have to be reground, but some watercolours can be reconstituted. Many manufacturers do keep old records and can give you precise details of their styles and contents.

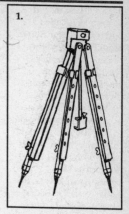

1. A travelling Victorian easel with telescopic legs that will adjust to various heights. The spikes make it useful on any soft surface, accommodating slopes in all directions. Practical as well as beautifully made in polished oak, any amateur or professional artist would be happy to have this. £55 and rare.

2. China palettes inside fitted boxes gradually replaced ivory discs. Miniature painters still prefer ivory or china for absolute clarity of colour. Most old china palettes have been broken, but they can be found now and then. They are worth buying not only for themselves, but because they can be used in restoring a fitted box. £12.

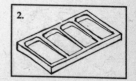

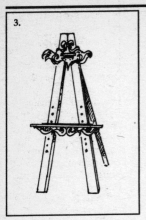

3.

5. Paint boxes are often heavily stained, hiding quality timber and joinery. This one was in a dreadful state. Remember these are working tools and look underneath the damage. Research should pinpoint the date and something about the maker; this T & R Rowney's Patent Pallet for watercolours, c.1800, was £100; in good condition, £200 or more!

5.

3. In complete contrast to the simplicity of the travelling model, this crested studio easel would have displayed the work of some notable Victorian artist. Prices from £99-900, depending on wood, quality and condition. This one is relatively restrained and needed quite a lot of elbow grease to clean and restore the pine. £88.

4. The Chinese made beautiful brush boxes of jade and porcelain. Here artists make do with japanned black tin. They are still practical, light and attractive, sometimes with engraved initials and fine leather straps.

Watch out for chipping around the rim and make sure the strap is secure. 1920-1930, £20.

6. Oil paint boxes carry far more than the relatively simple needs of the watercolour artist. They were often much heavier and almost always more elaborately fitted, as artists using this medium carry quite a lot of extra equipment. The substantial Victorian and Edwardian boxes had space for tubes of paint, as well as sections for bottles of turpentine and varnish, a big brush section for a number of brushes and, in the good quality boxes, a fitted wooden palette which could be removed, used for painting, and then fitted back into the box with a sheet to protect the rest of the contents from the wet paint. Sometimes there was even space to enclose a few small canvases within the lid. A modern equivalent would cost well over £150, if and when they are available from a few of the traditional artists' suppliers.

Look for good wood, well-made at the corners, and as far as possible undamaged interior partitions. Most will need thorough cleaning and then a coat of staining or varnish. Keep any old tubes of paint for research. Reeves, 1920s, £80.

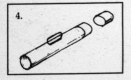

4.

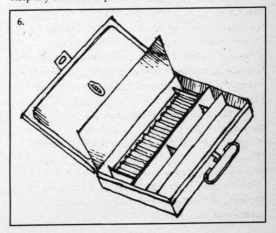

6.

Baby and Child Collectables

Baby collectables offer a double benefit because they make such wonderful gifts; few mothers – or – even more, grandmothers, can resist a tiny gown of white embroidered lawn, or an enamel teddy bear. (I should add, though, that the silver spoon shown here went to a buyer for her tea caddy!) Try not to let your instinctive pleasure at such delicate treasures overwhelm normal caution in assessing for condition and value.

COLLECTORS' NOTES

Any information about sources or family history does help to establish age and provenance, and it is easier than most with children's things, as photographs and anecdotes are passed from generation to generation. Buying from house auctions is especially fruitful if you can speak directly to the previous owner or the organiser of the auction. If you are seriously interested in a fine christening gown, for example, see if there are any photograph albums in the sale which just might show the gown in use. The same applies to rocking horses or other obviously well-loved toys or dolls and doll houses.

Christening mugs often have a family motto or crest on them - research there can make the difference between an anonymous piece of silver and a piece of history. Be warned that an engraved name on silver is considered unfortunate, while an embroidered name adds greatly to the value of a child's sampler!

Be careful, too, of fashionable over-valuation; old teddy bears of most modern mass manufacture may never be unusual or intriguing enough to bring serious money, though they may give your own family a great deal of enjoyment on the way.

Other toys and games can be found under different categories later in the guide. If you are buying as a future investment for a child rather than for your own pleasure, be particularly careful; silver is probably the safest purchase, simply because it is relatively indestructible.

1. The first precious gift a baby receives is likely to be a christening mug. Victorian and later examples are common enough to be a reasonable price; more ornate and heavier styles contain more silver and will obviously cost more. This relatively simple example, hallmarked 1903, has a cartouche for name and birth date. The silver is quite thin, but the gilt lining inside is immaculate.

Look for one careful owner! Dents from tiny teeth are not an asset. The hallmarks are often quite small and difficult to find, but it does make a great difference in value, even though plated designs were well made, with the same gilt inside, and designs were often offered in both sterling and plate. Today most buyers want a solid silver mug, and plate is always harder to resell unless it's extremely attractive, and with an unusual design or motif such as a children's nursery rhyme or fine engraving.

There are reprinted early catalogues which show a variety of mug designs; tracing your latest find can be very rewarding. London, 1903, £55 and up.

1.

2. Until c.1914, babies of both sexes as well as young children wore long white or cream ankle dresses. One clue is the size of the arm-holes; this is for a very young baby, and the length means it's a christening gown.

Look for fine lace without broken threads; thin lawn rips easily as it gets older, and tears lower the value a great deal. Avoid stained or yellowed fabric unless you are a good launderer. Faded and twisted ribbons can be easily changed, and missing buttons replaced. Prices vary considerably according to the quality and quantity of lace and embroidery. £35-70

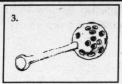

3. Rattles are a popular gift because they come in a huge variety of materials and prices. And older babies continue to enjoy the sound they make even more, when they can shake it for themselves!

Many had bells, as well as teething rings of coral, ivory, and from the 1900s on, of Bakelite. Today, , most silver rattles are bought to put away in r the display cabinet, and bright plastic ones are used everyday.

4. and 5. There is now a substantial body of reference works which anyone seriously interested in collecting bears must consider; See p. 193. But for the casual collector of one or two, look for known factories like Steiff in Germany and Merrythought here. Good signs are a long nose (modern teddies look flat-faced and cuddly) and arms, a slight hump in the back, and a growler. This is a middle-aged variety, Merrythought, 1940s, £60. Below him, an anonymous but elderly and well-used bear with embroidered hands and feet, and a deep growl. 1910, £35-55.

Baby and Child Collectables

Once a child has begun to grow up, there is a whole new world of appropriate bygones for the fond grandparent to buy.

Childhood really didn't exist until the much-maligned Victorians - before then, they were treated as miniature adults in every way. Even their toys were usually reduced examples of some adult preoccupation. Once Albert and Victoria were on the throne, with their deeply held convictions about the importance of family life and education, middle-class children were encouraged to play, to have books and toys of their own, and most would remember their early childhood with affection.

COLLECTORS' NOTES

Some objects exist in reasonable numbers; late 18th century doll prams are fairly common and at under £100. Look for iron wheels and handles, wood or woven cane bodies and thin brown velvet cushions or seats. Check that the spokes of the wheels are all in place, and that damage is confined to ordinary wear and tear. Most children were much more careful with their toys than our present generations, so good condition should be a prerequisite rather than a bonus.

Other kinds of furniture can also be found - many so-called apprentice pieces were actually made for children - and prices vary greatly according to the quality and finish of the wood. School furniture is less comfortable for the contemporary child, so it tends to be quite reasonably priced.

Children's clothes are now eagerly sought by collectors, and are usually found on stalls and in shops which specialise in white shirts, underclothes and household linen.

As with the dress here and the christening robe on the previous page, look out for damaged fabric. Iron marks are all too common, and they are very difficult, although not impossible, to remove. Be very careful - pure soap is best for general care and restoration.

1. No, not a teddy bear, but the Russian bear. This delightful enamelled small child's spoon of Russian silver was made around 1914 near Kiev. £55, because of its rarity in design rather than its silver content, although in fact it is quite heavy.

2. English seaside nostalgia - a wooden bucket and spade c. 1900, in perfect condition except for a few cracks on the blade. £25 the set.

3. A very practical Edwardian solution to every mother's problem; keeping food hot. This nursery hot-plate has a most unusual and delightful design of dancing ducks - surely enough to tempt any young child to want to see the bottom! This was an expensive piece of equipment- the metal base is of pewter, not tin, and its spout where you pour in the water still has its cover.

Some examples with Mabel Lucie Attwell or other famous illustrators' designs are way beyond our budget. An anonymous artist allows a better price of £30. Check for cracks in the pottery, especially radiating down from the metal rim. These have a depressing effect on the value, although leaks in the metal base itself don't seem to bother anyone. But a missing spout cover is difficult to replace.

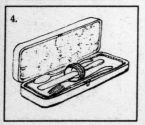

5. This relic of someone's school-days is pine, and relatively unmarked with ink. Those with attached seats are more expensive, but both are interesting for their social history. Look for an unbroken flap top, and a mellow patina on the wood. In good condition, as this one is, £35-45.

6. These dresses are just the kind mistaken for christening robes, but the large armholes give it away. This is for a child of four or five. In the 1920s, she would have worn a petticoat, white or cream stockings underneath, and white kid leather shoes. See previous page for advice about fabric condition. The fine silk embroidery is in pale pink, with a faded pink ribbon sash. £24 up depending on quality of needlework.

7. A pusher and spoon, beautifully engraved with Miss Muffet and a repoussé spider and tuffet! Birmingham, 1919, £60. There were often porringers, mugs and cups to match.

4. For an older child - knife, fork and spoon, complete with a matching napkin ring, in its original box. These sets are not very popular these days, which is quite strange, but it does give an opportunity for the shrewd collector to buy something at what I believe is well below its real value. A missing spoon or ring will take a hefty bit off the price. These were made in large quantities, so you could match up the set one day. Look for good-quality designs, heavyweight silver, and clear hallmarks. Birmingham, 1880, £60.

Baskets

Many countries take their traditional crafts more seriously than the British. There are still working basketmakers in almost every county, but it seems difficult to encourage us to cherish them.

The Basketmakers' Guild dates back to the 15th century, the craft originally based on the needs of the agricultural industry as well as domestic requirements. Willow is planted each year and gathered in the autumn when it is stripped and soaked to make it supple. Rushes are gathered from reed beds, shrinking in size but still just big enough to furnish a reasonable supply. The majority of basketweavers still gather and strip their own raw material.

COLLECTORS' NOTES

Victorian and Edwardian baskets are around in reasonable quantity, although early ones are rare. Garden and shopping baskets are hard to date as they may still be made. Agricultural or industrial basket designs were often scrapped when production changed, giving a "last likely" date for their probable use. This is a fascinating subject for a collection.

Condition is important unless shape or decoration is so rare that you can put up with frayed or broken strands. Repairs are common on the handles and the top edges; if skilfully done in the past, it will only affect the value slightly.

New willow is an unmistakable bright brown, and unless used outdoors, it takes years to soften into a faded beige.

Look for unusual shapes. Investigate modern makers; buy their baskets now and keep safe any information about them.

2. A small sewing basket with very fragile, applied plaster flowers around the everted rim. A fabric lining was originally tacked inside and a drawstring closed the top. The moulded rim makes this a real find; I've only seen one other basket like it; 1930s, £15-20.

3. A wastepaper basket with attractive strands of red and green braid woven into the centre. Dyed willow will give a good clue to age; it turns slightly grey. The rubbed and faded look of these colours indicate a date of at least thirty to forty years ago. £14-16.

1. Traditional egg carrier carrying eggs up to town from the country houses. The hoops are willow branches. Look for old prints and photos to find examples of locally made baskets. £35, quite rare.

2.

3.

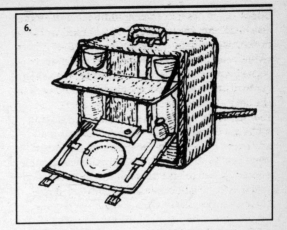

6.

4. An apple basket for the orchard workers; wide slats make a light but strong carrier for the pickers. The dark brown varnish is probably a recent addition and it does lower the value. Try to find one in original condition. £25, would be £40 if left alone.

5. Even simple everyday shopping baskets can vary. Look for attractive, capacious shapes and the use of different patterns in the weave. Wavy rims are good to look at and also strengthen the edge which takes most of the wear. Find local suppliers and see if they are reworking older designs. This 1950s example, still a bright brown colour, £9-12.

6. The aristocrat of baskets must surely be these fitted lunch and picnic hampers. The large example above was made for two people sitting opposite each other at a picnic table. Each side folds down for complete convenience and access to central food and drink compartments. 1880s-1930s.

Check leather straps and hinges for wear. Hampers like this have been made for a very long time, so dating and price is often related directly to the fittings. For example, an empty hamper could be only £20. If it holds a complete original china or Bakelite service, then over £90 would be reasonable.

8.

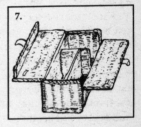

7.

7. A modest hamper with no fittings and only three compartments. They were made in their thousands for railway travellers as lunch boxes, and often sold complete with packed sandwiches and fruit. 1890s; £15-20.

Look for thermos flasks and sets of tin plates, cups and cutlery. Larger hampers could cater for up to twelve people.

8. A child's basket, with rope openwork down the middle. Traces of red and blue staining. 1880s-1930s. In demand from doll collectors as well. 1930s, £8-12.

Beads

Beads are an obsession with many women - the bead collector loves to show off her most beautiful or interesting finds. Because they are so ubiquitous, in so many shapes and materials, they are often very hard to identify with authority, so use a grain of salt when buying.

COLLECTORS' NOTES

Bakelite beads probably indicate a date in the 1920s and they are not cheap (see p. 130). Plastics were exotic, set in silver or gold much as some modern jewellers use the new acrylic materials.

Venetian millefiori beads were made from slices of paperweight glass rods. If the glass is trailed and dotted around the outside, it is probably French. Both French and Venetian bead manufacture is being revived today. The finest beads from the 19th and early 20th century are little jewels of colour and design; modern versions are clumsy and thick by comparison.

The best and most elaborateVenetian beads are expensive, and I know one collector who buys them individually, and has created a fantastic necklace with her finds.

Look out for unusual composition; I have a string of French porcelain beads dated by the shipping label to 1900. They were coated in lace before being put into the kiln. The residue has left a fascinating pattern burnt into the china. Look out, too, for unusual designs, like the Edwardian string (**2.**, right).

Metal links are more likely to be original, not a necklace made from left-over sections of broken strings. But there is nothing wrong in restringing - everybody has to do it for their own jewellery sooner or later; as always, it's just that you should know what you are buying. Learn to restring yourself; it's not difficult, just fiddly, and well repays the effort.

Metal links do have one fault - they are easily pulled apart, and a string dropped in your bag at a fair can be in three parts by the time you get home. So wrap them carefully in paper first.

1. A group of varied beads, most from the 1890s to the 1920s. Without a particular style or design in the stringing, it remains quite difficult to date them more closely than that.

A: Malachite chunks, a small string probably made for a young girl. Malachite is now often ground down to make the powder for artists' colours who want to reproduce the old Malachite green used by earlier painters, so the strings are getting difficult to find. £20-40, depending on length.

B: Fine cut-glass beads with long metal gilt stringers. These can make a collection on their own - they come in almost every colour. Check that the glass is not plastic - it should feel rough and sharp at the edges; the shapes and cutting of the beads will vary a lot. £8-15.

C: Oval clear Venetian glass, each bead wrapped in other colours. These are much cheaper than the millefiori beads in which each rod hs to be made up from tiny assembled designs. Look carefully to see that the alternating ovals and small round shapes are consistent throughout the string. The metal links are easily broken and then beads can be lost. 1900s-1930s. Clear ones like this £15-25, depending on length and attractiveness of the colours. The millifiori beads are still being made today, and they can cost up to £45 or even more for a short string.

D: Whitby jet, £30. Whitby, in Yorkshire, was the source of most of the finest jet mined in Victorian England. The Victorians used it for everything from tiny bead embroidery to huge double and triple strings of beads as big as marbles, plus hat pins, fringes, book covers, rosaries, etc.

E: So-called "fossil coral", with the tiny holes which give it its name. Much less expensive than chunks of smooth coral, but I think much more interesting. Around 1930, £85.

F: Ivory discs interspersed with tiny coral beads. c.1910, £25.

2. A most unusual string of beads, made up of rock crystal and wine-tinted glass, set with triple rings of gilt.

The asymmetrical style lets us date this pretty accurately to the 1930s, and it was a complete steal at £10. Expect to pay at least £25 if you can find one - I've never seen a design like it before.

3. The original gilt thread of these moulded glass beads has frayed. It will have to be restrung, which is expensive. You can have it done, but almost certainly not as in the original; the gilt thread was not only knotted but then wound around the knot. Not an easy repair, but the c.1930 glass moulded beads in the shape of scarabs are in very subtle and unusual colours of dusty pinks and cloudy turquoise, well worth the £18.

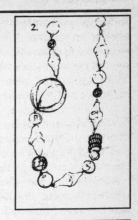

2.

3.

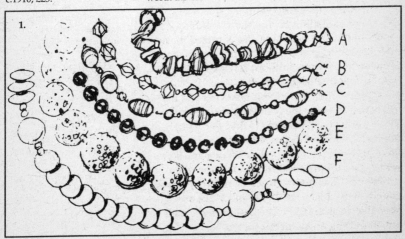

1.

A
B
C
D
E
F

Biscuit Tins

Packaging in an attractive container is not new; transfer printing and lithographic colour printing were used to decorated china boxes almost as soon as the techniques were developed.

Printing on tin, a method perfected around the middle of the 19th century, resulted in a fantastic assortment of tinplate toys. It's not surprising that Huntley and Palmer were the first company to realise that their products would last longer if they were marketed in air-tight tins; Mr Huntley's family had a tin factory next door.

Within a short time there were tins holding all sorts of products. The plain utility of protection was forgotten in the rush to attract customers by appealing to the "value for money" instincts of every good Victorian housewife. Such decorative boxes also made a perfect present, so much more tempting than plain paper and card. The term Biscuit Tins is generally used to include dealers and stockists of all kinds of tins, including chocolates, cigarettes, and so on.

COLLECTORS' NOTES

Look for good clear designs and as much of the original colour as possible. The manufacturer's name is an asset; on the best-quality tins they were hidden under the base and/or inside the lid. Sometimes they run up on the side.

Unusual modelling is important; anything pretending to be something else is prized more than a straight boxes. There are tins in the shape of chests of drawers, fold-out sewing boxes, lighthouses - the list is endless.

Condition of the printing is also vital and it's important to know the rarities. Many general dealers don't have the time to find out. There are not many reference books, but there are quite a few knowledgeable and specialist dealers; if you are serious about collecting, get to know them.

Tins are still common; biscuits, cigarette, and cough-sweet tins of the 1940s and 1950s are available at under £3-5. The best ones are well worth putting away for the future.

1. A sweet tin in the shape of a sundial, with a motto lettered around the hours, and cupids dancing amidst the sun and moon up and down the shaft.

The dial itself folds down to prevent damage in storage, but it has made it rather weak and without repair it won't stand up as it should.

This delightful tin is one of Huntley and Palmer's - it's marked under the lid - which gives it some age but the colour, which was a lovely sage green and gold, is severely faded.

In addition to being painted, the design was impressed on both the dial and on the shaft; a mark of quality. The poor condition is reflected in the very reasonable price for such a desirable design; £35-40. With more colour on the pattern it would be double that at least.

2. A box of toffees as a biscuit barrel, with a willow-bound handle. Marked on the base and inside the lid with the manufacturer's name .

The delicate oriental bird design has faded reflected in the price of around £20; 1930s.

Be careful of rust; if you are not very careful you can clean away the design as well as the rust patches.

If you use your tins, don't have them re-tinned inside, it will completely ruin their value. Line with greaseproof paper and check regularly for damp.

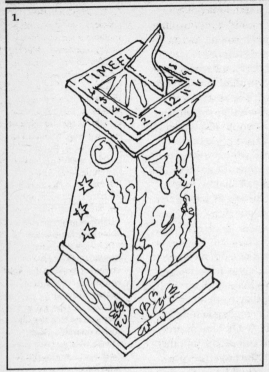

1.

3. Cigarette tins were made from the early 1900s, right up until the 1960s. Most held fifty or a hundred, and were appropriately decorated with advertising for the tobacco company. Others, like this souvenir model with a scene from Loch Lomond, were designed for future use on the dressing table. A paper case (still inside) kept the cigarettes well packed. You may find the most interesting and unusual examples on the stall of dealers who specialise in advertising rather than biscuit tins. 1920s, £18-20.

3.

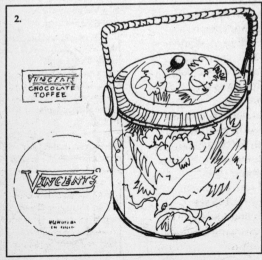

2.

VINCENTS
CHOCOLATE
TOFFEE

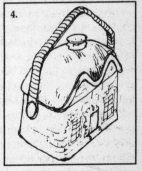

4.

4. A modern box as a cottage, imitating the popular ceramic wares in thatched cottages. Although brand new, it's well worth putting aside. £6.

Bottles

A bottle collector's market is different from almost any other; table after table of brown, blue and green bottles looking very similar, and many with the crust of recent burial still upon them.

Even more astonishing is the number which look very like the ones in your larder at home, yet which are searched for avidly and relinquished with sorrow at another fair offer.

Bottle collecting is inextricably connected with rubbish tips where most of them are found, and we might imagine they are like the brown sauce bottles we are likely to dig up in our gardens. But they exhibit a whole panoply of shapes, forms and sizes, as full of human history as they were once full of the necessities of our lives.

COLLECTORS' NOTES

Bottles were made in tough glass, often coloured only with a little oxide to hide the impurities. Very old bottles were blown free-hand or more usually into a mould. Later they were mass-produced, very much as they are made today. Some buyers are only interested in blue or green or amethyst bottles for their colour, putting them up on shelves against a window to achieve a stained-glass glow in a kitchen or hall.

There's more serious interest in bottles as containers; collecting medicine or chemist's bottles, or food products, or drinks. A refinement is to focus even more on a particular maker within a period. If you become really hooked, research at local factories often turns up surprising amounts of information.

Related subjects also attract bottle collections; people who collect children's things often add feeding bottles to their search, kitchenalia collectors like preserving jars and doctors often enjoy collecting medicine bottles.

Be very careful of chipped rims and bases. Thick, dark glass makes it difficult to see damage; I've missed large chunks and quite big cracks because the general texture of the glass was so rough and ready.

1. These small but decorative bottles were in every Victorian medicine cabinet filled with a variety of drugs and treatments. Commonly ribbed (to avoid slipping through feverish hands, perhaps) they are usually rectangular or octagonal. Their cork stoppers have long since vanished. Any with intact contents would be a real bonus. 19th century, £3-7.

2.

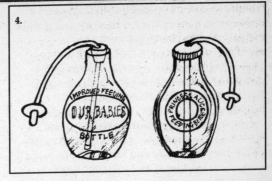

4.

2. A very different kind of medicine bottle; this is a treasure, with its painted and gilded label and the original stopper, c.1850. At chemist shop size, this would have been one of a set, and finding such a group would be a real achievement.

Look for pasted labels, too, with instructions. Similar bottles in milk glass or other colours are even more rare. £50-60 ea.

3. For robust use in a travelling bag, doctors' equipment was sold with bottles cased in a wood cradle or in a metal sheath.

This may have been a veterinary surgeon's bottle, to be poured down reluctant animal throats, and therefore extremely strong. A fitted vets' bag or medicine case would be very valuable indeed. C.1900, £65.

4. The revolution in child care made it acceptable to bottle feed, and had the side effect of creating a new industry. Babies' feeding bottles offer the interested collector a whole range of shapes and sizes. Many designs were patented to provide an extra marketing fillip to the manufacturer. Marks are commonly embossed on the bottle itself, making identification for the collector a little easier than usual with bottles.

Collect a group of different shapes; these are 19th century. Others are banana-shaped for use in the cradle. Look for complete sets with their rubber tubes. £12-25.

5. A group of old beer bottles, preferably with their fanciful labels intact, would be collecting with a lite touch. Most collectors specialise by concentrating on one brewery, one region, or a particular period. Happily the history of Britain is redolent with brewers' yeasts, and their literally thousands of vanished brews. Obviously those bottles still intact would be most interesting, but avoid drinking the contents. Look for embossed names or labels to help identification; local records often help. 1890, £25.

5.

Boxes and Trunks

Nothing can be more useful than things in which to put other things! And so, from the beginnings of domestic life, boxes and trunks have proliferated in every form. There are tiny boxes of wood or paper to hold even tinier pins, pennies or potions. There are medium-sized boxes for personal belongings of all kinds, including papers and photos; and of course, there are those wonderful trunks whose size and stability make a mockery of our modern nylon duffle bags. With care and attention, our entire lives could be stowed away in appropriate boxes.

COLLECTORS' NOTES

Since the choice is so wide, it is essential to narrow your goals to either a material or a purpose. Some people collect silver boxes for every purpose, some collect writing boxes and slopes of whatever material. Make your own decision, but do stick to it, or you'll be overwhelmed by temptation on every side!

So many boxes are empty squares; look for information about its purpose as well as the usual details of material and date. A fine leather-covered box with an expanding base is more interesting and more valuable when you know it's a glove box than if it's simply a box. There are often clues in the box itself - the smell of tea from an old caddy, a few fragments of paper from a stationery box, and so on.

Watch out for missing decorated hinges which would be difficult to replace and expensive to copy, but don't worry too much about keys which can be easily cut to fit the lock.

Most boxes suffer damage at the corners. If you become seriously interested in the subject, take a woodworking course and practise your own restoration. It's amazing what can be done, and while professional help is expensive, your time can be a bargain.

Splits in solid wood are more difficult to repair than veneering. Canvas covering can be patched like wallpaper, but it will always show.

1. Lacquer handkerchief box decorated with flowers; smaller sizes were for pins and needles. A key kept fine linen safe. The scalloped edges were damaged easily; watch out, too, for mis-matched tops and bases. This late 19th century one, £30-35.

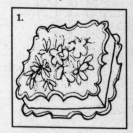

2. A late Victorian mahogany writing slope; these went everywhere with their owners, and suffered accordingly. Watch out for damaged corners on the inside as well as out.
Those with plain compartments can still be found under £100. Figured woods with brass inlay and complicated fittings can reach £300 to £400 or more. If the box and lock is in good condition, the leather slope itself can be easily replaced. £85.

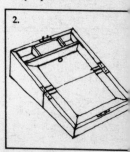

3. Contemporary enamel box on copper, numbered and signed, by Halcyon Days. The tradition of enamel has been revived recently. Make sure it *is* enamel, not ceramic; limited editions are the safest buy until you know the field. £50-90 or more.

4. Trunk for colonial use in the tropics; lined in zinc, it protected the contents from insects. Sturdy wooden slats and iron corners did the same during long journeys. Interesting labels add to the fun. Look for unusual ships or lines. 1920s, £35.

5. Hatbox with folded top hat inside. Ladies' bonnet boxes were wider than men's. Look for solid edges and ties still in place. Labels are fun, but ignore new "Victorian" scrap-covered fakes which are being made in quantity. C.1880, £45.

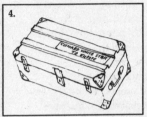

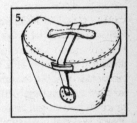

6. At the first sign of spring, Victorian or Edwardian households put winter clothes and other heavy things away until they were needed in the autumn.

Camphor blocks kept wools safe from moth, but their smell was no more attractive then than it is now. Hence the tightly lidded box which would retain the odour - and its potency - inside. For the historian of domestic life, a box like this is only worth collecting if its labels and contents are intact. £25.

7. The aristocrat of luggage, the wardrobe trunk featured in every pre-war Hollywood film of glamorous stars on the high seas. But they were essential for anyone on a transoceanic voyage lasting weeks or even months, and dressing for dinner every night. A high society couple might have two or even three, with their silk linings, many drawers, pockets, shelves and built-in hangers. Together with a dressing case, you could be ready for anything! A collection of these would require a lot of space, but one could be the focus of a group. Look for complete interiors with all their sections in place, secured linings, and look out for rusty fittings. £85.

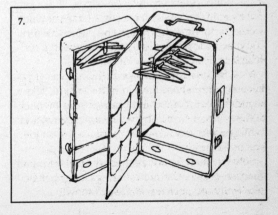

Brass

An alloy of copper and zinc, brass has been made at least since Roman times, but the metalware we know today in a hundred and one guises dates largely from the 19th century. New methods of casting, stamping, varnishing and colouring had made it into a maid-of-all-work, found everywhere from cellar to the attic even - in its most malleable form of gilded pinchbeck - in the jewellery box.

COLLECTORS' NOTES

Brass as a material is very difficult to date, unless you are able or interested enough to make a chemical analysis. This alone makes it particularly liable to reproduction. When you add the ease with which old pieces can be recast in modern moulds, then you can see why the shops and stalls are filled with brand new "antique" trinkets. These are theoretically tourist souvenirs, and dealers will tell you so. But a dealer may not always know the source of a more unusual piece, so it's important to understand what to look for, even if you will not always be infallible.

Learn from the best; museums and specialist dealers have genuinely old brass. Look at the colour and at the patina, acquired only after generations of handling and polish.

Look at the dirt in the crevices and on the back. It shouldn't rub off easily. Brass signs, hooks or door furniture usually have some flakes of paint on the back where it was attached to woodwork, and may be turning slightly grey or green with verdigris from dampness or corrosion.

Look for finely detailed casting, and places where continual use has worn the surface. The centre of a knocker where hands naturally touch will be smooth and detail will have worn away. Handle a piece as if it were in use, and look to see if your fingers fall on worn places.

Modern reproduction is shallow and simplified because detail, even in multiple casting, costs money. Look for sharp, detailed modelling.

1. The manufacturers of brass articles followed the fads and fashions of each season. When the majesty of nature was all the rage , the brassmakers were there with appropriate objects like this letter rack. This Monarch of the Glen might have hung on would-be baronial panelling next to the front door, or even on the new tartan wallpaper. The design is completely flat and stamped out of brass sheet, typical of north country manufacture; patterns included ducks, hunters and other high Victorian fancies. Other kinds of flat brass outlines were used for inkstands, coat racks and key holders. Look out for pieces broken off the top, or unnaturally spiky edges where the metal may have

1.

been dented. 1870s, £25. Letter racks make a fascinating collection, easy to display and very useful. There are letter racks of copper, wood, and other materials, as well as those made in papier-mâché and tinware.

2. Letter boxes may seem a prosaic purchase for a collector, but the right period door furniture can transform your house. Look for brass handles and door knockers, too. This Victorian box has a lovely deep patina; make sure it's big enough for modern use. £25-35.

3. Letter scales were an important accessory when people often gave their letters, already stamped, to the delivering postman. Small, elegant scales like these were made for the home; for office use there were bigger models. Some are still with their original cases, which would add to the value.

Look for a complete set of weights, and sometimes a matching stamp case in brass. Letter scales can be identified by the flat tops

4. Of all domestic scenes, the image of a brass kettle singing on the kitchen hob is one of the most evocative. Yet working kettles were usually made of copper or cast iron; brass was reserved for the drawing room.

The Dutch example shown here is a case in point; it was not intended to be used over a fire, but would have been filled with tea before being brought into the sitting room and left to keep warm by the side of fire. The handle is off centre, presumably to help hold it straight when the kettle was filled with hot water.

This particular model was imported into England in considerable quantity, and some experts have suggested that it was never intended to be used at all, except as a decoration.

In fact, the handle is very comfortable, the body holds a considerable amount of hot water for lots of refills, and the little feet would have kept the bright brass off the coal-dusty hearth. This one, c. 1880, £60-80. Watch out for bad dents on the body.

The nicely shaped grip on the handle is opal glass, and slightly chipped which brings it into the lower price range; others had amber glass, white or cream porcelain, or wood.

Pottery handles with Delft designs in blue and white are modern tourist souvenirs.

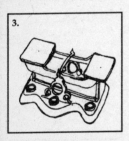

of each balance. 1920s, £35. Small kitchen scales which might be confused with them have a scoop instead. For other letter accessories see Inkstands, p. 90. There are really interesting brass accessories: you may find a brass sprinkler-topped pounce pot for drying ink.

Brass

Colour is important; modern brass is very bright and it's been lacquered to keep it that way, even in outright fakes, because it's easier to keep it looking attractive. Genuine old brass has a duller, deeper glow from years of tarnish being polished away. Unfortunately, sometimes genuinely old pieces have been lacquered by their owners to make cleaning easier for themselves, making it harder for buyers to judge.

Fakers also leave tarnish on in order to create "old" patina, but handling pieces professionally dated in museums, and known to be antique, will soon show you the difference.

Another clue is over-supply; when you can see the same object more than once at a fair, it is almost certain to be reproduction.

The popularity of brass early in the 20th century suffered from previous over-production. Victorian brassmakers of Birmingham and Sheffield had piled up thousands of articles for house and home; it isn't surprising that brass lost its fashionable appeal for a while.

The Arts and Crafts movement was in love with the mediaeval world, its dark wood, bronze artifacts, and especially its subtle pewter and copper tones. Gilt and brass were suddenly thought cheap and vulgar, to be made use of in plumbing or in the kitchen where necessary, but not anywhere else. "Bold as brass" was not a compliment!

So it is quite difficult to find interesting, good-quality decorative brass until after the chrome and white fads of the 1930s; it is also likely to be hammered from sheet as pewter and copper were, rather than cast.

Keep a sharp lookout for all small brass items in early 20th century styles - boxes, ashtrays, cigarette cases, etc. They have distinctive hard-edged geometric designs and linear engraving. At the moment, these are still rarely reproduced, although one exception seems to be a pin box in the shape of a fly, which is turning up in quantity.

1. An Edwardian reading light attached to a clip. We think modern designers are so clever, but this tiny lamp was bought way back in the 1900s for a nurse in one of the large hospitals, presumably to keep the light level low during the night shifts. A remarkable and ultimately useful buy at £25-30.

WARNING:
Never use any old electrical equipment until you have had it checked out by a professional. Many lamps still have very early wiring which will certainly have perished; even 1950s replacements will be extremely dangerous by now, especially when the lamp has a metal base through which the wires pass.

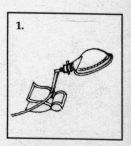

1.

2. A little cast brass door knocker in the shape of a ship. 1930. £15-20.

The detail is quite extraordinary, including sailors, a castle and a whole series of little waves.

3. Crinoline ladies have always been wildly popular with the makers of bric-a-brac. They have been turned into lamps, pincushions, figurines, of course, and in the 1940s even loo paper covers. But here the wide skirts are the perfect shape to act as bells.

Look out for different faces and costumes. There really is an amazing number of variations on what is basically a very limited theme.

The man in the top hat is unusual, though not necessarily more expensive.

Unfortunately, little trinkets like this have been much copied; signs of reproduction will be bright yellow brass, combined with over-dark areas from dirt in the grooves, to simulate age. £10-15 each.

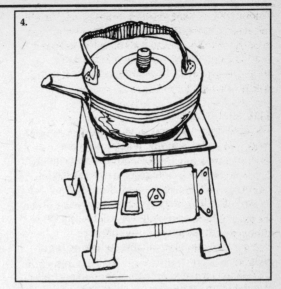

4. A travelling kettle and stand, Secessionist period, made in Austria around 1910. The stand has stained-glass panels and a separate spirit lamp. The geometric shape and linear decoration are typical of this style. Watch out for dents: the metal is hammered rather than cast, worked as if it were copper, and being thinner than usual, it's easily damaged.

Check that all the pieces are there (the spirit holder often gets lost) and as far as you can, that they match, are in the same style and look right together. £95-100, more if signed or marked by a known designer or maker.

5. A Victorian pestle and mortar set, used by a chemist rather than in a kitchen. Look for natural wear where appropriate; this set was so well used that the inside is quite distorted. £55. Pestles also come from this period on stoneware and wood.

Cameras

Taking pictures has become a symbol of modern life. The tourist hung around with cameras is now the object of scorn, but in Victorian days the new and exciting technology had the same snobbish appeal to the avant garde as virtual reality has today.

COLLECTORS' NOTES

The early plate cameras of wood and brass used large glass photographic plates and were designed for professionals. But the first camera to really popularise photography was the Kodak Brownie Box Camera, named after Mr Brownell, its inventor. It was cheap, very easy to use and it had rolled film, also widely available. By 1914, there were at least two dozen or more inexpensive models available for taking family snapshots.

Zeiss in Germany, among other makers, raised the stakes by adding an adjustable focus and a wide range of speeds, while the Brownies kept to their basic appeal of "Bright" or "Cloudy" days.

After World War II, the world of photography had changed out of all recognition. One of the finest was the Zeiss Contax 35mm camera, with a built-in meter, coupled range-finder and all sorts of other goodies which put its price in 1950 at well over £100 - today about £1,000. For more modest collectors, read about the Russian copy, the Kiev, which happily is very affordable.

Serious collectors should make use of one of the many reference books which gives basic information on factories and dates. For those interested in taking pictures as well, the most vital points to check are the shutter mechanism, the winder and the lens.

Bellows tend to get worn where the folds are; open the back and hold it up to the light to make sure they are lightproof.

Concentrate on a single make or even a single mark like the Brownie; the variety of models, plus contemporary albums and advertising can build into a fascinating collection.

1. Plate camera, originally with glass plates coated with photographic emulsion. These were made from c.1850, and with the glass replaced by film, they are still being made today because the size of the negative gives remarkable portrait and art shots. Look for fine wood and heavy brass fittings. This model, c.1910, £70.

2. Salex reflex camera; the image was reflected off an interior mirror and thrown up for the photographer, who looked down from the top onto the ground-glass screen. C.1900, £50.

3. One of the very first Brownies, reaching the world in 1900 and with all the faults of a first try. The strap wasn't comfortable, the winder was tiny and fiddly, and the front clips soon rusted away.

But a revolution had taken place, and an amazingly little £10 can buy you a piece of history.

6. No apologies for another Kodak. This ingenious Vest Pocket Kodak of 1928, only 6x12 x2.5 cm, includes a built-in stylus to mark the film as you finished taking your photo. It was a great success with travellers for its compact size and reliability. £40-55.

4. The improved Kodak Brownie model 2, c. 1914, with bigger winder, shaped handle and a better clip at the back instead of the front. Kodak also decided on coloured Brownies in cream, red, and blue - a decision that almost cost them the market when it failed dismally. It would be a better buy today. Model 2, in brown or black, £12-15, £50 in colour.

7. The Contax cameras made by Zeiss had been a great success before the war. At the end of 1945, the Russians carried back Leica equipment to produce their own Zenith and Kiev. Fascinating story and a good camera. This Kiev, c.1960, and a very reasonable £35-40.

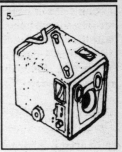

5. The final post-war Brownie, with bigger view-finder, more technology yet with the same ease of use. It will still take good snapshots provided you can find the film and two rollers. The roller is a different size from the ones used today, and you need two: one empty, one inside the film. This has a flash, too. £20-30, depending on having at least one roller.

8. Zeiss Ikon Nettar 510/2, made in post-war Germany. A modern light-weight roll film camera, which folded up into a reasonable size, although at 8x16x4 cm, it was considerably larger than the Kodak. However, it does have a self-timer, so that you can run in front and join the group! C.1950, £45-50.

Chairs

In the history of early furniture, chairs have a particularly sumptuous place; to be seated was a mark of honour and respect, a luxury in a world which was otherwise on the move or lying down. A long way down the scale were the utilitarian seats of rural industry, like milking stools, now sought after and prized for their evocation of a simpler age. But nostalgia apart, all kinds of stools and chairs are still bought for their original use, so considerations of condition and repair become vital. Affordable chairs in our budget range date from the end of the 18th century at the earliest, and most will be much later, from 1890.

COLLECTORS' NOTES

Earlier generations sat facing forward and with feet on the floor. We are a careless lot, abusing chairs by lounging on our spines, rocking on their back legs, sprawling sideways, leaning back, or standing on them to reach high shelves. It takes solid workmanship to deal with all that, and if you add the drying and shrinking power of central heating, when buying for use, the first quality to look for is stability.

Look carefully at the join between seat, back uprights and legs. If the uprights extend directly down into legs, the chair will be stronger than if the chair has its uprights and legs fitted separately into the seat. Spindle-backed chairs are sturdier than those with two uprights, because the spindles share out the load of your weight leaning against them.

Dried glue in loose joints can be fairly easily replaced but it will need clamping to make sure the joint stays fixed. If any part of a joint is broken, the chair can become very unstable, and an entire new part will have to be fitted.

Look carefully at the bottom of the legs and the back of the seat. That is where woodworm often begins. A bad infestation in the past, even though cured, may have made the wood too fragile for normal use.

Watch out for modern reproductions which are often distressed or perforated to simulate old woodworm holes. It isn't that reproduction is bad in itself, but you should know what you buy.

1. Country-made furniture was always slow to adopt new fashions. This makes dating by style very difficult, as popular details continued in use for decades, even centuries, after city styles had changed.

This fruitwood chair could have been made at almost any time from the late 18th to the late 19th century. The back is a simple ladder, and the stretchers are just as straightforward. The signs of a craftsman are there nonetheless; there are tiny finials on the top of the rails, the rush seat is firm and capacious, the arms have a pleasant curve. It is, in all senses, a comfortable

Above right (top detail): the finial has been carefully finished off and the arm struts curve delicately into the seat. Someone was determined to do a little

design. But there is one surprise: its low stature. If you think a chair has been cut down, then look at the legs - sometimes woodworm shows up there first, But these legs are sturdy, well turned, and unmarked.

The rails are also correctly positioned on the leg; if the legs had been cut down, they would have been abnormally low and looked awkward.

Perhaps it was made as a fireside or nursing chair. Whatever the origin, it's in perfect condition, lovely warm-toned wood, neither repolished nor restored. Individual chairs like this are a find. 1780-1820, £80-90.

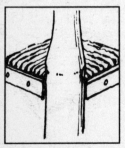

better than usual. Yet the front strip, no more than a nailed slat protecting the rush seat, (detail above), is very crude, with gaps on either side.

2. Balloon back dining chairs are typical of the Victorian period. They are curvy and comfortable, with overstuffed seats which are conveniently easy to re-upholster.

Matching sets in fine woods such as walnut are now quite expensive - over £400 per chair! So it makes sense to collect singles, which you can still find in mahogany and rosewood for much less. C.1850, £95-100.

1920s reproduction is a good alternative; the wood, usually of good quality to begin with, has had time to acquire a warm patina.

Look for original fabrics; there is a new market for period textiles. Hand-embroidered needlework covers would be a find. Reproduction of the 1930s is often poorer in quality as the depression took its toll on crafts and materials.
For 1920s reproduction, you can pay no more than £50-65. They are good buys.

3. Michael Thonet, working in the mid-19th century, utilised an old technique of shaping wood under steam pressure. Millions of his simple bentwood chairs were sold all over Europe, so that in spite of their age, you should be able to find a basic one for £25 or less. With a Thonet label, or as an armchair, £50. Thonet himself used only solid beech. Later in the 1920s and 1930s, others used laminated wood. Many early Thonet chairs have cane seats. Later, pressed plywood seats became popular. Thonet also made tables and small desks, etc. Designers like Alvar Alto have taken up the scrolled bentwood theme - their work is very expensive!

4. Footstools are still easy to find. Look for quality in the wooden frame and those nice round feet that slide on the carpet. Many had embroidered covers, now these can be more valuable than the stool. Victorian, £35-55.

Chairs

Replacement feet are common on heavy chairs because that's where the damage occurred on stone, irregular or damp floors. The signs are similar to those on chests of drawers or cabinets; an unexpected break in the line of wood grain travelling down from the seat, or a style which somehow doesn't quite look right.

Checking on original condition in fully upholstered chairs by seeing the frame before you buy is not usually possible. Underneath the fabric, there may be three or four kinds of wood, and odd repairs over a long period. Unless you are hoping for a period treasure in disguise that shouldn't really matter, as long as the repairs have been well done.

Standard rush seating is quite easy to replace, but it is not cheap. However, with the present taste for rustic styles, even upholstered side chairs where the covers were badly worn have been adapted to rush or cane. Except for early rustic chairs, if the seat frame is in a different wood, it was probably meant to be upholstered, or at least hidden under a cushion.

Thonet bentwood chairs were manufactured in such substantial quantities that they are still in almost every café and restaurant across Europe, and piled up in thousands of dusty attics. An example of a good idea making very good. But watch out for where the scrolled wood may have split; it will have to be glued together, and the increased tension creates problems.

Arts and Crafts chairs made c.1880 to 1910 have been gaining in price recently and they now bring a substantial sum. They usually have a square section for the legs, sometimes tapering up to a slender high back, and a cut-out motif of a heart or an elongated tulip. Oak was a favourite wood, stained to honey or darker, perhaps with some painted roundels. Look at the books of chair designs by William Morris and Charles Rennie Macintosh. They will give you a glimpse of the style, so you can spot one hidden amongst a standard Edwardian group. Museums hold catalogues of furniture makers at the turn of the century which will be helpful, too.

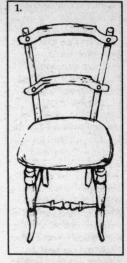

1. Very pretty turn of the century chair, a light top with Victorian legs. Ivory pegs hold the top rails in place. A bedroom chair, too fragile for the dining room, which may account for the reasonable price of £160 the pair. Look for similar singles which can still be found for £60-70. Here the upholstery had been re-done in linen. Remember to take that into account when buying.

3. The ubiquitous kitchen chair which has been made for 100 years or more. Mostly of pine, or occasionally in beech, it has been found painted, stencilled, cushioned, lacquered or even finished in black and gold. Modern imports abound but they are quickly recognised by heavy legs and struts, and an orangey gloss and a polyurethane finish.

The two side struts, placed just a little forward, make this one more comfortable and stronger that most. And at most, £45. But for good examples, with a better patina £65. Collect a set.

2. This Edwardian chair is very adaptable. The sides are sturdy but pleasantly canted back, the legs taper nicely and the rush seat, although not new, has aged well. Since many similar designs were made it's easy to build up a set. They were painted later for the kitchen; check that the paint doesn't hide major damage. £40-50.

4. A design that mixes elements from almost every period between 1410 and 1910.

The simple lines and light fluting on the straight, tapered legs are pure Regency; the black lacquering and gold trim is Victorian, as is the mother-of-pearl motif in the tiny floral inlay at the top of the front legs.

The back is taken from mediaeval drawings with its square leather panel tacked up with bright brass studs, and the panel of openwork below is back to Regency taste.

And yet, against all reason, it actually looks quite pleasant as a dining chair, neither too heavy nor too brash; a set would be quite a good-looking addition to any room.

If you found only one or two, it would be next to impossible to gather a set by chance when the

design is so eclectic, but you should be able to find similar shapes, with straight panelled backs.

One strong feature is the workmanship. Make sure it hasn't been traduced with bad varnishing or clumsy repair. In lacquer finish, £90. In plainer oak, with no inlay, £60.

5. An unusual folding chair of bamboo, probably made in the East for travelling familes from the British cantonment. The simple action is still in good working condition, although the wood itself has split and become discoloured over the years. It came originally with a matching cushion in heavily embroidered wool which has long since disappeared. Around 1918, £38-50.

Chairs

During the early part of this century, the very quality of Edwardian furniture was its burden. Always being judged against 18th century originals, the lightness which is its strength was then mistaken for feebleness and weakness.

Today the circle has turned and we appreciate not only the craftsmanship but the adaptability of much Edwardian furniture.

Art Deco chairs are still easy to find, and with their much heavier geometric shapes, nothing could be further from the classic elegance of Edwardian style at its best. In the past five or six years, the Deco image which has been appreciated in the ceramic arts for some time, has finally struck a welcome chord in the minds of some furniture collectors.

The three-piece suite made its first real appearance, and the square, solid construction of the chairs, often in thick curved walnut veneer, is very heavy. Many people, including myself, love the period in other forms but not in upholstered furniture! Side chairs are, perhaps, more adaptable, but be warned - the real period pieces are often extremely heavy and difficult to move.

In the late 1940s, another change began with the use of resins and plastics developed during World War II, translated into industrial design. The first glass resin furniture is now eagerly collected and the best pieces have brought very good prices when in original condition. Within a few years the moulded plastic furniture of the 1950s and 1960s will no doubt join them.

Look for satinwood and floral motifs on Edwardian furniture inspired by the Adam and Sheraton styles, particularly along the tops of chair rails.

Much solid Deco wood has become cracked with the growth in the provision and temperature of central heating. Chairs must be in good condition to keep their value. Original cream or white leather upholstery is a bonus.

For 1940s and 1950s furniture, check on the differences between the various plastic materials.

1. The Lloyd Loom company, still in business, developed a woven paper fibre wrapped around a core of wire. It was cheap, light and it furnished the nurseries and bathrooms of Britain in the 1930s. Some pieces have gilded edges, tastefully fading into the pastel base. Chairs, tables and laundry baskets were made; look for the original label - there were other makers, too. £25-45.

2. The corner chair, a useful space saver. This classic design adorned Edwardian halls and reception rooms, ready to hold the casual visitor or telephone caller, or be pulled forward when company came. Make sure there are no breaks in the slender struts. £65.

3. The Edwardian version of the classic kitchen chair on the previous page. How much lighter and more delicate every part is. The legs rise and narrow to join the seat, the arm supports curve ever so slightly down and the tall back, with a hint of the Mendlesham style, looks - and is - so comfortable! £65-75. To make sure you have an Edwardian and not a 1950s chair, look for the quality in the detail.

3.

3. Detail

4.

4. and 5. Left and right; two examples of 1930s' ingenuity in reworking traditional styles and motifs. On the left, a compressed Chippendale with its extended top rail and long central slat. The Arts and Crafts-influenced trellis, right, is a later classic, now popular again. £45-55 each.

5.

6. Glass fibre chair by Charles Eames, on a steel base; 1948, for Herman Miller. A few years ago, this might have ended up in the dustbin. You can recognise glass fibre by the "shredded wheat" look of the underside or at a worn corner; the glass fabric has been soaked with resin. Injected and moulded plastics are smooth on both sides.

Look for a matching cushion, and the Herman Miller label underneath. £15 if no one else sees it, £500 if they do.

6.

Clocks and Watches

Time is wrapped up in the very beginning of recorded history, but time-keeping and the development of clocks really began in the West with monastic life, around 1300AD. Iron clocks using weights gradually turned into brass clocks with springs, and the huge older clocks shrank to being portable belongings, to be treasured and handed down in families as important heirlooms.

Clockmakers have long traditions; for many collectors the greatest revolutions were the new pendulum of 1657 and the hair-spring for watches in 1670. Compared to these, later changes are mere ornamentation.

COLLECTORS' NOTES

Unfortunately, 18th century clocks will be generally well beyond our limited funds, but there are a surprising number of 19th century clocks and watches at affordable prices, even though the movements are unlikely to be very sophisticated.

The British have always been fascinated by the scientific problems of clockmaking, and British cases tend to show off their solutions. French clockmaking, it has been said, is the history of French furniture all elegance and decoration, while German and American factories made sober, useful clocks for accurate time-keeping in kitchens and shops.

The collector on a budget must accept the mechanical limitations, and concentrate on the variety of cases for good, simple movements. An alternative is thinking functionally - clocks as toys, clocks as different alarm systems, watches for sports, and so on.

There is very little reference material available for most of these less expensive clocks. Factory history becomes important, where all kinds of records and production notes might be available. Newspapers and magazines offer considerable information. For those with an orderly mind, a collection illustrating the history of watchmaking tools would be a fine challenge.

1. An American clock c.1880, possibly made by Ingraham & Co, but unmarked. The US was suffering from European competition at the end of the century, and they began turning out huge numbers of highly decorated designs to suit every taste. C.1880, £75, bought in Suffolk.

2. In England the craze for chinoiserie has always been strong; this pleasantly scrolled 1880s lacquered mantel clock would have graced a modest but stylish home. With the painting slightly faded, but working, £65. In better condition, £85.

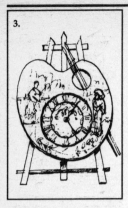

3. One Victorian catalogue offered seventy-five mantel clocks - this "artistic" easel in painted wood had a cousin sold with a real brush! The clock was not working, so the price was only £20. You can find contemporary replacements easily, so don't be tempted to put in modern works.

4. A Swiss fob watch with beautifully engraved case in two colours of silver, with intricate floral design; so many were made that it costs only an amazing £25 or so. C.1900.

5. The simpler styles of Art Deco after 1920 were taken up quickly by those clockmakers whose clients had fashionable homes. This lucky horseshoe mantelpiece clock came with two carved wooden horses , shown parading with their jockeys, but they were sold off separately, lessening the value of each piece.

The engraved plate on the back confirms this was a prize in a local race; that alone would add to the value.

The wood is natural oak, the figures are gilt, and the lettering is in the open "moderne" style. Look at the back to see if the mechanics have been changed. The clock alone, £45. As a set, well over £150.

6. A ring watch, first made in the 17th century, copied in gilt and paint of the 1960s. The watch is still working though the gilt has faded. A good £12's worth of time.

7. For the sportsman, a French diver's watch of 1960. One of the first of its kind, so £72.

Coffee and Tea Paraphernalia

Coffee and tea are both imported drinks which have become necessary to this country in different ways. Coffee houses, the late 16th century version of our coffee lounges or bars, were soon established in all the major cities. The most famous result of their popularity was the institution of Lloyds insurance, named after one of the coffee houses where investors and brokers met to do business. Our word for those more informal restaurants, called cafés, is, of course, the French term for coffee.

There exists a myth that the British don't know how to make coffee, and that drinking coffee regularly is a Continental vice. As the above dates show, coffee houses were here just as soon as the fruit of the tree was known in Europe.

Within a few decades coffee was served at home after dinner, and soon replaced hot chocolate for breakfast in fashionable households. Reading any of the hundreds of 19th century cookbooks and household advisors, it is clear that no man was expected to go out to earn a living without a cup of good, strong coffee inside him.

COLLECTORS' NOTES

For the collector, the history of coffee has created a whole host of utensils and serving pieces. There are all the various utensils mentioned on the right, as well as an infinite variety of pottery and porcelain pots and cups. Look out for very early little cups called cans, presumably because of their straight sides without handles. These were the first coffee cups, but by the 18th century, this was abandoned for the traditional handled coffee cup we know today.

Then there are all the related collectables; advertisements, shop tins, old recipe books, trays, prints and so on. Every one of these areas can turn up a coffee-related subject to add to the more obvious kitchen and dining room equipment. The assiduous researcher can easily build up a collection of social, artistic, and not least gastronomic interest!

1.

2. and 3. Small domestic coffee grinders are clues to the change from exotic drink to household staple. Cookbooks of the 19th century assumed that coffee would be made every morning, and after dinner. They exhorted their readers to roast their own berries, with a knob of the best butter to keep the coffee beans from burning. Even those who bought their beans already roasted were told to grind only what was needed, just before use.

Both precepts are still encouraged today.

No. **2** is English, c. 1880, made of oak. It has a drawer, and its original handle. £25-32.

No. **3** is the same date, probably German or Austrian, and much more decorative with barley-twist carved legs and an open shelf where a bowl would sit. £40-45.

Look for clean metal, without rust, and smooth turning action. The knob of the handle should match the wood or the

Coffee

1. This Victorian iron coffee roaster may not even be recognised by a non-specialist dealer. It was a sturdy tool, not a decorative accessory, and it was made to last. The struts at the base fitted into bars in front of the open fire.

Look for labels or manufacturer's trademarks or registered numbers, but you're not likely to find either until Victorian times (c.1848) onwards.

On metal utensils you can ignore surface rust, although deep-seated patches may have destroyed the base, and the whole roaster may fall apart. Check that the metal is solid under any top gunge.

C.1880, iron with brass fittings; only £25, but quite hard to find, so be prepared to pay just a little more.

4. Some early canisters were made like tea caddies with locks, but later, just air-tight metal tins were acceptable. This unusual tin in blue and white enamel has three compartments for different varieties. Not valuable for itself, but a real find for the social history collector. C.1910, £15.

decoration - they have often been replaced.

When you clean grinders be very careful not to leave damp areas inside. You can dry them by leaving them in a warm linen cupboard for a few hours.

5. A Susie Cooper pot of the 1930s, typical in its shape, like an inverted pear. It is one of the distinguishing marks of coffee pots; another hint - check that there is no tea leaf strainer inside the spout. The Deco style is shown in the flat spout and matching finial on the lid, and it would have come with a sugar basin and a cream jug. On its own, £45; £70 for the set.

Coffee was served with hot milk, and the jug would have been taller and more slender than its equivalent with a teapot.

Morning coffee sets

include a small coffee pot, a small sugar basin, a hot milk jug, one or two cups and saucers, and also a matching tray.

Coffee and Tea Paraphernalia

Tea, originally from China, has been an obsession in Britain for many years, although surprisingly it arrived around the same time as coffee in the 16th century. But whereas coffee somehow became associated with sophistication and glamour, tea was the family drink, soon outstripping its rival in general popularity. Every year, the fastest ships, called Tea Clippers, carried newly fermented leaves in the large wooden boxes called tea chests. Later on, when trade with China was threatened, tea was grown in India to make sure that the British would never lack for what was by then *the* staple drink.

COLLECTORS' NOTES

Canisters for tea were stored at home inside a decorative tea chest. Individual canisters, now called tea caddies, were sometimes made with locks. This was intended to keep the fragile leaves safe from servants who might use the tea in their own teapot.

Caddies were made in every material, including glass; affordable silver or silver plate caddies date from the end of the 18th century or later. They are particularly delightful in lacquerware, with decorative Chinese or Japanese painting considered appropriate for the oriental leaf.

Tea pots, tea kettles and tea cups are familiar to most collectors; tea strainers are a more unusual subject, and come in a remarkable variety of shapes. They are also easy to display in a collection. Enamelled tea labels for boxes and canisters came in at least four basic versions: Black, Green, Hyson and Bohea. They make another interesting subject for a collection although they are now quite rare.

The tea ceremony was and remains an important ritual in Japanese life. Round or oval jars and other utensils sometimes appear in British markets. These are often imbued with great religious and family significance, and can be of great artistic merit.

1. The tea caddy as a compartmented box, with separate lids for each section. This one, of red lacquer with a floral design, is particularly attractive as the fine painting has survived in remarkable condition.

A lot of lacquer was imported during the 18th and 19th centuries, so the objects themselves are not particularly rare. Badly damaged surfaces, with rubbed or poorly executed paintings and little or no gilt decoration intact are not worth buying unless they have some special attribute, like a signature or a very unusual subject.

Lacquer is not often understood in this country and if you are interested enough to do research and study the best examples in museums, there is no doubt you can make some worthwhile purchases. It's hard to date without study, as the desire of most lacquer painters was to copy the past masters. 1860s, £95 in top condition.

Animal Models
Cast-iron umbrella stand, a heron with outstretched wings ready to spear a fish. Some are painted, the heron in white, the fish in many different colours. This is a 1930s reproduction, so only £75, but it is finely cast and well finished. An original early Victorian one, £250.

A Wheildon pottery sheep. If undamaged, at least £250 or more. With one ear missing, £100. If you want to collect Wheildon, then worth it for study of the pottery, its body and style of decoration.

Child Collectables A game of table croquet, but surely not even an adult could be tall enough to play with those mallets on a table. Carpet croquet, with tiny mallets for young hands. Complete, and c.1915, £12.

Baskets A huge wheel basket for gathering herbs or possibly for cheeses. Late 19th century, in good condition except for one missing slat. £65.

Biscuit Tins Assorted tins 1930–1950 showing how wide the variety is even today when so many metal containers have been replaced by plastic and card. All of these are under £15 at the moment, and many at car boot sales are under £5, so look out for unusual shapes and designs. Remember that advertising tins have their own collecting fans, but I would go for the box intended to house your playing cards later (lower right) and the octagonal box with a lovely Art Deco tree just above it.

Boxes A simple mahogany box of elegant slimness with a paper lining that has been stencilled and then hand-painted. Possibly a jewellery box, although they usually have a fabric lining. Cards? Stationery? C.1910, in perfect condition and not French polished either, and complete with a brass lock and its key (not shown). £28.

Brass These hall and wall fitments were the Edwardian answer to clutter on the table. Almost always backed in oak, the brass patterns make a wonderful assortment of period lettering and style. And you can use them, too, for the very purpose they were intended for! 1910–1920, £18–28. Make sure the hinge is still tight and secure.

Coffee and Tea Paraphernalia And it could also be brass. A little gem of a bell which came on a tea tray. French, its elaborate moulding is both beautiful and crisply cast, the bell has a delightful quiet ring, and altogether the most civilised way I've ever seen of summoning more hot water from the kitchen. C.1890, and an expensive £68, but what class.

Copper A large, outdoor copper lantern of immense presence. Very little ornamentation, just perfect proportions and a louvred top to allow the gas vapours to escape through a series of tiny holes, just visible in the picture. The glass is original, with the wavy slightly yellow look of late 19th century industrial glass; modern replacements are sure to be very clear and clean with no imperfections. The copper has oxidised nicely to a dark brown, although it is not yet green, so perhaps it hasn't been outside for the past twenty years or so. You'll need an appropriate arm to hang it from, once you've paid £65–75.

Costume Jewellery Assorted pins and necklaces from the 1950s. Some have enamel decoration (the pair of earrings and the necklace far right); some feature those big brash glass stones and huge drop pearls so typical of the period. Prices £15–75.

Cutlery Two unusual carving sets with horn handles. The set on the left with quite stubby cream polished handles is older, around 1880, so well used on tough meat that the knife has become twisted; £18. The boxed set on the right is later, the handles were as rough as they are today, but the silver bands are hallmarked and the box makes it a presentation. 1925, £32.

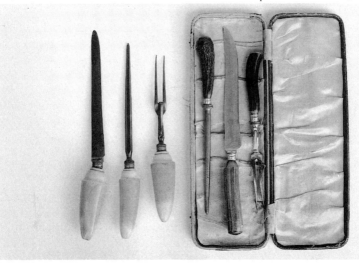

Dolls As so many of the better dolls are now very expensive, this is one way of collecting for tomorrow. A modern doll, about 20 years old, if that, but made with immense care and attention to detail. Her hair is plentiful and soft curly blonde, her eyes open and blink, and her dress is a Victorian child's outfit, with real lace edges to the ruffles, matching underwear, and tiny kid shoes with mother of pearl buckles. Look for just such details and put them away as heirlooms for the family. This one, only £35–45. Even if you think the dress is cotton, as this is, be extremely careful in washing as there are often contrasting ribbons which might run.

Embroidery A beadwork cushion in the most beautiful autumnal tones of browns, greens, and old rose. The design is a little odd, because the beadwork bouquet is quite elaborate and typical of Victorian Berlin work design, while the background is a rather odd abstract in blending tones. Although the centre is certainly 19th century, I would be inclined to say that the bouquet may have been taken from a beaded footstool and transferred to a cushion which would suit a more modern home. However, it was certainly done some time ago, as the background wool has also faded. So an old marriage, perhaps, but still the beadwork is in very good condition, the design is quite lovely, and the combination has been finished off with an appropriate piping and tassel. £95.

Garden Ornaments An amazing pair of plump, lazy cupids. They are terracotta, not very well done by fine art standards, but they have a robust charm very like the Staffordshire pottery figures of the same period, the late 19th century. Firing such huge pieces must have been an adventure in itself, for they are two feet (60 cm) long each, and almost as high. But they have survived undamaged without a crack or chip.

Somehow I feel they might have been made as a single job for a particular place, probably along the two low walls of a small set of steps. Possibly Italian, and very difficult to date, anywhere from 1890 to 1930 would be a guess. Just under our limit at £98, they would add a sense of humour and relaxation to any garden.

Glass Above, a pair of pressed glass purple spill vases, decorated with Prince of Wales feathers. The glass is so dark it's almost black, very typical of mid-Victorian design. £55 for the pair – they're perfect, and finding a pair is not easy.

Right, a slightly later piece of Victorian glass in the naturalistic mode of the 1880s. The flower is so thickly painted that it stands out from the surface. No chips, good marbling on the glass and a reasonable £25.

Gloves, Hats and Handbags Above, a wooden glove box covered in fine silk and painted in a faintly oriental design. Middle-class women spent hours each day in producing decorative objects for the home. Some were very talented amateurs, and this box is extremely well painted although not quite oriental enough to be authentic. C.1910–1920, £22.

Below, a contemporary ivory and paper fan for the evening bag; it's only 6 inches (15 cm) long and painted professionally this time; £22. Interesting to the fan collector because of its size and the openwork on the ivory. Probably Chinese.

Inkstands and Desk Accessories Above, a
wonderful dark wine plush-covered writing
box, with swing-out sides holding two
bottles of different coloured inks,
compartments for writing paper and
envelopes, and even a blotter. There are
elastic holders for pens and pencils in the
top. C.1880. I've never seen a plush
stationery box before, and this is unmarked
and in very good condition. 1880, £85.
Check that the ink bottles really do sit
properly in their holders, and that the tops
match the bases.

Right, a paperweight of rough agate cleverly
adapted to a grey sea, with a black marble
thermometer. C.1990, £42.

Kitchenware Above, a black cast iron bread basket. No doubt the manufacturers could say with certainty that their products would last, but the idea of using heavy iron for something as light as basketwork has a certain perversity.

However, it has been suggested that these were made specifically for homes in deep mourning, and with the predilection the Victorians had for turning whole houses into shrines to the past, it may be as good a reason as any. The openwork iron was very well done, the intricate moulding has been well cast and well finished – there's even a broken reed at one side. 19th century, £45. Watch out for reproductions which are roughly made.

Cheese making was a great art in the Victorian kitchen, and these perforated moulds were in constant use for the soft white cheeses which we have only recently begun to appreciate and make commercially again. After the cheese had begun to coagulate it was hung in a muslin cloth over a dish to catch the excess water, and then, when only just set, it was put into just such a mould to finish drying and setting into the pattern. Watch out for chipped edges. £65.

Lamps and Candlesticks A pair of wooden twist candlesticks, of particularly fine proportion and beautifully figured walnut. Most examples are in brass or oak, so the wood gives this pair an extra value. C.1880, £90. Look for smoothly turned stems – some are quite clumsy and look unbalanced. Watch out for splits around the sconce and signs of burning inside the candle holder. If wax is allowed to burn down right to the base, it will damage the wood, although it's unlikely to catch fire. Dating of this style is very difficult, as they were made for a long time, and are still being made today. Look for the patina on the wood to help you.

Linen and Laundry Above, a large size tablecloth worked over the whole surface in open threads and then embroidered in blue. Drawn threadwork was a favourite of the embroiderers because it was relatively easy to do. A coloured lining might be laid underneath to show up the work.

Edwardian magazines gave two or three patterns for drawn threadwork each month to make at home. 1920s, £75.

Below, a simpler and much smaller tea table cloth with a fine Ayrshire white work border. £35.

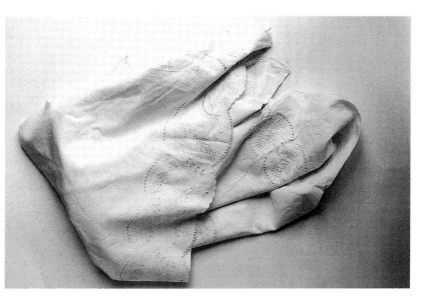

Metalware Above, a fine pewter coffee or chocolate set made in the 1930s. They are unmarked and may be French or English. The handles and spouts are beautifully cast, and the octagonal bodies are in very good condition, without any serious dents. Pewter can be quite soft, and some old pieces get to look very battered. £55 for the pair, and well worth it.

Below, a tôle tray, probably for bread. Painted tin ware was often japanned in black enamel to resemble lacquer. Now getting rare, early 19th century, £95.

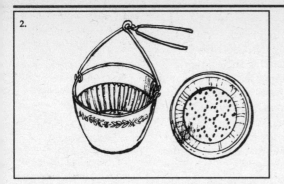

2. A silver tea strainer, both side and top view. Two springy arms fit directly into the spout; tilt the teapot, and the strainer hangs beneath to catch any stray bits. Most strainers are held while you pour and are then set down on a stand. Some ingenious inventer thought this was a much better idea, and I agree! 1904, Chester. Gilt interior, too. £65.

3. Those who could not afford fine caddies stored their tea and coffee in air-tight tins (see Biscuit Tins). These have an attractive marbled design in different dark colours, and appropriate labels. A set of three is good; a complete set which includes flour, baking power and smaller ones for salt and pepper is even better. Check the inside for rust. For some reason many French canister sets, in tin and especially in pottery, c.1930-1950, are around in the markets now. The best include labelled tins for dried fruit, etc. £8-45, depending on number of containers, design and condition. Blue and white colours, stylised designs, or unusual labels beyond the standard four or five are always at a premium.

4. Tea urns are generally more expensive than our limit allows, but just occasionally you can find a really good urn at an affordable price.

This one of copper with brass trimmings is quite impressive. See Care and Repair for pushing out any bumps, examine the seams and areas around the handle rivets that might leak.

Check that the tap matches the side handles; all too often they have been twisted off and lost. to be replaced with another pattern. C.1882, £98.

Copper

A marvellous material, with its warm, glowing colour and malleable enough to take the most detailed design, copper was probably the first metal mined and worked in the ancient world. At the beginning it was seldom used on its own, but as an alloy with tin to make bronze and later with calamine to make brass and its related alloys, paktong, pinchbeck, Britannia metal, etc.

During the 18th century it was fused with silver to make Sheffield plate, but that was superseded in the 1850s by electro-plating.

Although a very good conductor of heat (think of all those warming pans!) it cannot be used without a lining for cooking as it corrodes easily and produces poisonous oxides in contact with acid foods.

Copper was also covered with gilded and enamelled decoration to make miniatures, little boxes, ornaments and all sorts of trinkets, like wine labels and menu holders.

In the home, copper, which cannot be cast, was associated with hammered and wrought 18th century kitchenwares. During the 19th century it lost out to the newly improved brass casting, relegated firmly to the servants' hall and cottage decoration. In our new enthusiasm for traditional and period homes, copper wares have spun right back into the market and good pieces in undamaged condition reach premium prices.

COLLECTORS' NOTES

Most of the copper articles which we see today at reasonable prices date from the late 19th century. Country smiths went on making useful things for local families no matter what fashion decreed.

Copper is very soft and it dents quite easily. Many copper utensils were mounted or handled in brass for coolness and for strength. And since the pieces were usually hammered into shape in the first place, it is relatively easy to push dented or bent copper back into shape, provided you can reach the front and the back of the damaged part.

1. The copper kettle sums up in one image everything we imagine about the past; a tranquil countryside, dotted with sleepy villages and inhabited by contented families.

Small wonder that old kettles in good condition are now scarce and expensive.

Look for a pleasantly rounded shape, either an oval as in this example, a circle, or less commonly a hemisphere. These were made flat at the back, to fit closely against the grate, or flat-bottomed to get the most heat into the water as quickly as possible.

In the earliest examples with wooden handles, the seams were folded and hammered together; after the mid-18th century, the joints were soldered. Later on, they were made without any seams. The simpler the shape, the more straightforward the handle, the earlier it is likely to be. Glass and ceramic handles were popular from the 1840s onwards.

The typical Victorian spout curves up like a cobra; Edwardian makers favoured a straight spout rising from the base.

Signs of pitting are a good indication of age, but not necessarily of origin. We used to send shiploads to the Middle East; now they are sending some attractive examples back to us. 1840s, £80-100.

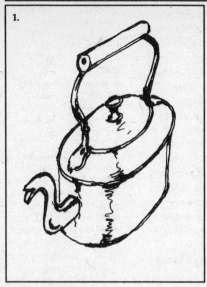

4. A measuring jug. These come in a huge variety of shapes and sizes; the best examples like this one are marked either inside, or more normally outside, with the various amounts to be measured. £20 for one, £80 for a set, at least three.

2. This little moulded copper bird is typical of locally made utensils which added a decorative touch to an essentially functional object.
Sitting on top of a heavy lead weight, it was used in the kitchen to press pâtés or terrines in a matching earthenware pot. The eye has been enamelled in yellow for an extra touch. Probably French, c.1880, and with its base, £35-45.

3. Most collectors think of moulds only in their more decorative forms (see right) but cooks needed a large supply of simpler shapes for individual portions of everything from mashed potato to vegetable timbales. These very useful moulds are heavy copper with intact tin lining and they were bought for £1 each. Impossible to date.

5. There are over 500 jelly moulds in the Pavilion kitchen in Brighton; unusual pictorial designs are eagerly collected. Modern reproductions are generally far too clean and shiny. Try making jellies in an old one and in a modern one; the old mould will give far sharper results. According to condition and scarcity of the design, £35-350!

Copper

Copper came back into fashion with the Arts and Crafts period, as the rich glowing colours of the mediaeval world were in fashion everywhere in the house.

It was particularly adaptable used as plaques or inlay on furniture. William Morris and his fellow designers used copper to make motifs and pictures let into framed panels, often above tiled backs or within the leaded-glass doors of cabinets and sideboards.

Copper was also useful in their art institutes, set up to help amateur and working people enjoy making things for themselves. At the Keswick Institute of Art and other places, copper was utilised for trays, vases, jars, even entire tea sets. The forms were relatively easy to make in the soft metal, and the finished pieces were sometimes left in copper and sometimes coated with silver plating.

The workmanship was necessarily fairly crude, but the inspiration and excitement gives many of these pieces a robust style of their own. Although known designers and artists of the Arts and Crafts movement have become rightfully esteemed and therefore expensive, the Institute pieces are sometimes marked but seldom signed and often unrecognised. This is a rich field for the collector willing to go out on a limb and trust his or her own judgement.

With the growth of Art Nouveau, copper again found itself used for the decorative effect of its colour and the ease with which the metal could be hammered into rich and complex designs. Most Art Nouveau pieces are in repoussé work, with the same motifs and designs familiar in other materials. So far, copper Art Nouveau has not been well reproduced because the work is so complicated, but no doubt as prices rise they will find a way. Look out for modern copies hand-made in Asia where labour is not a problem, although the designs don't quite achieve the free flow of the originals.

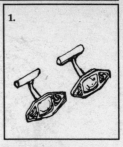

1. These cufflinks were originally buttons, their centres filled by a glorious mix of red, green and blue enamel. The backs were fitted later, but they are also copper and very well made. c.1910, £15.

2. A finger plate, c.1900 with every detail of the period. Copper is so soft that these plates were sometimes bent in two. Look for tell-tale cracks and distortions. One, £15. A set of four, £75.

3. At home the tablecloth was brushed after the main course and before the dessert by the servant or the hostess. Small, elegant dustpans and brushes were kept especially for this one purpose, and they were made in a bewildering variety of styles and materials. Copper ones are fairly unusual and this sinuous Art Nouveau pattern with its matching brush is a pleasant find.

Wood brushes and pans are quite common, many are mounted with little brass rings or copper inlay. The brushes tend to get very tatty and this will make them unsaleable unless the handle design is something really special.

Other solutions included a kind of flat server which scooped up the crumbs. They were considered tablewares and were mostly made in silver and silver plate.

For brass or wood, only £15-18; in copper with a distinctive design, £35.

4. and **5.** These two flower vases demonstrate the change from the curves of Art Nouveau to the geometrics of Art Deco.

They also show clearly even in this outline drawing how well the metal could be used to adapt to any style. In the first, the repoussé work is perfectly adapted to the motif; in the second, the hand-hammered surface matches the hard-edged design.

Both are English, No. **4.** around 1910, £65; No. **5.** c.1925, £20. The different estimate lies in our current preoccupation with the Nouveau period, and the fact that the simpler Art Deco objects are not yet recognised nor esteemed to the same degree.

6. A curious spoon. It took a fellow dealer to recognise the design. The original pattern in silver is well known, capped with an Egyptian scene adapted from a wall painting in Tutenkamun's tomb.

This may have been a cheaper copper version, or the base for a plated finish. C.1923, in copper, £12, in silver, £40.

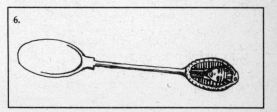

Costume Jewellery

The wish for personal adornment is hardly new, nor was it sexually oriented towards the female of the species until the Victorian period. Tribal burials often contained beads, a fancy toggle or a bracelet, and from what we know about early societies, the men were as avid in their enjoyment of jewellery as women.

Wearing fake or costume jewellery is a scarcely younger fashion - almost as soon as glass had been discovered, around 2000BC , there were elegant strings of "turquoise" beads and earrings of green "jade" and gilded pottery in the marketplaces of Egypt and Mesopotamia. Unhappily, such precious examples are not for modest collectors (although there are some really good copies in museum shops).

Poorer customers, as always, had to be satisfied with make-believe; gilt instead of gold and glass instead of gems. At first such gewgaws were little more than something bright and shiny, but as metalworking techniques improved, so did the quality of the deception. Until the 1950s, most deliberately fake (as opposed to inexpensive) jewellery was *intended* to deceive.

COLLECTORS' NOTES

Victorian costume jewellery was quite low-key, and largely female. One level below gold and diamonds, semi-precious stones and silver were used, and below that came the clever but inexpensive use of decorative materials considered appropriate for very young ladies or the poorer classes.

Aluminium makes its appearance coated in gilt, or silvered to resemble fine metal useful for the long, heavy chains used for watches, as well as for strings of beads, pens and pencils, and so on.

Costume jewellery brooches of the period had simple loops on the back with no safety catches. Pebbles and stones were set in silvered metal, mosaics and carved bog oak were great favourites with discreet and modest spinsters.

1. Entwined hearts are a typical Victorian motif, with fond and sentimental meaning.

This particular one is typical of the Luckenbooth brooches, made in Scotland of silver or silver plate. Some date back to the 18th century, but this one is c.1850. They were given as engagement presents or as good luck charms for travellers. In plate, £45, in silver £75-80.

2. For Victorian men it was especially important to look respectable, no matter how limited your budget. The gold "sleeve links" of the prosperous man of business were copied in gilt metal for his clerk. This design was illustrated in 1880; £12.

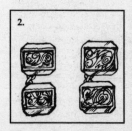

3. Short strings of beads were worn around the neck, under high-necked collars of ruffles or lace. Longer strings had lockets or pendants to keep them hanging straight down. Inexpensive Vulcanite beads might end in a real jet pendant. Now the Vulcanite is more sought after than the jet; see Plastics, p. 130.

Since mourning jewellery was required for any lady on so many occasions, black beads and earrings were essential. Jet was relatively expensive, but black glass looked just as good. In fact, it fools quite a few collectors today. Glass will feel lighter and colder to the touch, and the cut edges will be just a little sharper than jet.

Look carefully at the clasp, if there is one. Glass beads were usually threaded with gilt or white metal or silver plate. Jet more often had sterling silver or gold settings, and individually knotted · beads.

This glass bead triple rope with metal clasp, £20. A similar jet string £60-90, depending on the clasp.

4. Mosaic art was a tribute to Ancient Rome; this brooch has a mother of pearl central motif. Look out for missing chips. The pin, like all costume jewellery of the period, has a plain metal loop with no safety catch. C.1870, £20-30 depending on picture quality.

5. Watches of the Victorian period required elaborate accommodation both on the wearer and in the house.

A man's waistcoat flap had its special buttonhole to anchor the watch chain. An extra small chain in a matching pattern, called a fob, hung straight down from this, often finishing with a seal and a little clip for the watch key. Then the long chain looped across to the small watch pocket on the other side. This gave an air of garlanded sobriety to the owner.

At home a watch stand stood on the dresser for use at night instead of having a mantel clock.

The Albert chains, as they were known, were named after Prince Albert who had popularised the style of wearing them outside the pocket, across the waistcoat; Albert chains were also made in lighter designs for ladies to wear with their tailored costumes. The finest were made of 9 or 15 carat gold, or at the very least, sterling silver. Watches and chain sets were carefully handed down from father to son, or mother to daugher.

But the respectable clerk without an inheritance could buy chains and fob chains in gilt metal and silver plate. These two, one with a fake seal and one with a miniature portrait are light and pretty enough to have been for a woman. £15.

Costume Jewellery

A great change in public taste came about when mass-produced Victorian prettiness turned to the spare, hand-made style of the Arts and Crafts movement, and then to sinuous and often suggestive curves of Art Nouveau. Fashion demanded silver glow instead of golden glitter, muted colours of blue and green, opals and moonstones instead of diamonds, and irregular, uncut pearls instead of perfect round spheres.

These complex designs required a high level of craftsmanship, but studio artists, even in the finest ateliers of Asprey's or Boucheron, found they could create magnificent and often superior effects with glass and enamel at a fraction of the cost of traditional precious gems. For the first time, truly splendid objects were being made from affordable materials.

Within a few decades, fashion changed again to favour the popular jewellery designer even more. New plastics and the geometric motifs of Art Deco were just what the public wanted, and these simpler shapes could combine mass-production with sophisticated images.

COLLECTORS' NOTES

Art Nouveau jewellery has become very fashionable, and at the budget level it is sometimes over-priced; a known style label often encourages the inexperienced customer. However, protection lies in the value often being in the workmanship rather than the materials, so reproduction is very difficult to do well; cheap copies with clumsy awkward curves and blobby details are easy to spot.

Look specially for marks, signatures or custom-fitted boxes with the name of the maker. Enamel motifs are characteristic, but watch out for damaged edges, sometimes repainted, which seriously affect the value.

Art Deco prices are beginning to climb, but there are so many unrecognised pieces still around that the prices may stay affordable for a while. Look for a trademark on the back.

1. A delicate pendant in sterling silver, hallmarked only with one stamp, with a central pearled boss and hanging pearl, and with wings of silver-gilt. Pendants like this were immensely popular during the period, often made for young ladies as a first grown-up present. 1895-1910, £50.

2. Liberty pins were copied constantly. They turned the exotic curves of Art Nouveau into something intrinsically English and natural. This silvered metal and blue enamel brooch, 1910, £15.

3. The quintessential Art Deco woman; a cloche hat, a shawl wrapped around her coat with hanging tassels and the absolutely fashionable accessory, a Borzoi hound. And all in a few square inches of silvery chrome.

Art Deco jewellery has many strong features, and this pin, a copy of the miniaturised figurines we are more familiar with in bronze, shows three important ones; the angular style, the use of the feminine face and body carried over from Art Nouveau, and the liking for chrome.

Look for a good clean line on the back as well as the front. Chromium plating has a deep grey glow rather than the whiteness of later imitations. I have seen two versions of this, one with an ivory face, one with an enamelled face; 1930s, £35.

4. Bakelite was a symbol of Art Deco, often used in fine jewellery.Prices have fallen lately, perhaps as supply exceeds demand. These hairclips are all plastic, and only £6 each.

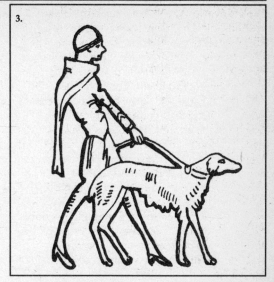

3.

5. A true vestige of the past when every dashing young woman carried her cigarettes in a little bag. This unique compact and cigarette case in turquoise enamel is decorated with the beloved quartered circle on the edge in black enamel and diamanté. The entire piece is only a sliver wide and it probably had a slightly clumsier lighter to match - petrol lighters weren't as technically refined as they became later. In its original suede case, c.1929, probably American, and a very reasonable £80.

4.

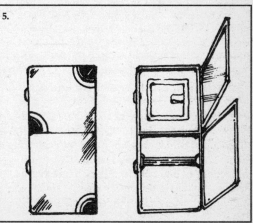

5.

Costume Jewellery

During World War II, frivolous fashion and costume jewellery were severely restricted. Not surprisingly, as soon as the war was over a new burst of creative energy swept the entire fashion world, especially in Paris, still its headquarters and chief source of inspiration.

Christian Dior created the New Look, yards of once-rationed fabric gathered into skirts sweeping the ground. Tight waists, short gloves and smart hats - in time, women who had learned to be comfortable would turn away from so much structured prettiness, but for the moment dresses and suits were nipped in, padded, collared and widely lapelled. The perfect setting, of course, for pins and necklaces. By now couture houses knew how much of their future would lie in accessories - perfume, lingerie, handbags, scarves and costume jewellery.

In America, too, top designers saw no reason why their clothes should publicise other designers and they joined the name game. Every show featured the master's distinctive touch of that season, be it jewelled hats, white bracelets or dancing elephant pins.

COLLECTORS' NOTES

Look at pictures and sketches of the Paris and New York shows during the 1950s and 1960s, where most of the best costume jewellery was made. Newspapers and magazines usually keep libraries and their articles often carried a mention or a photograph of some new jewellery fad. Trace whatever you can through the old catalogues of individual companies as well.

Study the best designers and manufacturers. In Paris costume jewellery was a speciality of Chanel and Schiaparelli; in New York Oscar de la Renta was only one designer who had entire collections of big, bold jewellery made every season. So far signed pieces are seldom faked, although the designs are often copied. So far.

1. This Oscar de la Renta parrot looks quite refined, but in fact it is as big as your hand, and made from very large and heavily foiled pieces of red, blue and gold glass, with a large pearl eye.

Look carefully at the back to make sure the foiling isn't damaged, since that affects the way the stones will glitter. There were half a dozen parrot heads made with various feathers and patterns; collecting a group of similar pieces always improves a collection. 1950s, £75.

2. A 1950s version of the ubiquitous Victorian name pin. Silvered metal, stamped out with the name in gilt. £12.

3.

4.

4. Butterflies were only one of many animal and insect figures which were extremely popular. Any colourful creature was adapted into a lapel pin. Just as bright as the butterflies were ants, bees, crocodiles, lions, even ordinary blue flies and red ladybirds.

Stylish naturalism was the vogue, and the geometric symplicity of Art Deco forms was long out of fashion. Look for realistic detail but fantastic and exaggerated. Sometimes the colour came from enamel, but here it's from glass cabochon jewels and gilt. Marked Napier; c.1964, £75.

3. Little figurines like this ballet dancer were extremely popular during the late 1950s. They were usually made with an amazing amount of detail - this one has extra stones on the tutu to give additional texture, a little bracelet on her arm, and even a tiny tiara at the back of her head. But she is not marked, which keeps the value down to £15-20. Look for that level of craftsmanship.

Other figures include little girls holding baskets of flowers and a Roman goddess draped in white enamel with an detailed crown of tiny emerald bay leaves.

The combination of enamel and glass was favoured; work by Georg Jensen in sterling silver and enamel is beyond our limit, but unsigned Scandinavian pieces come onto the market at £50-90.

5. All was not colour; the ever-popular plain gold or silver bow continued its success throughout the years almost unchanged. This gilt assortment,1950s-1970s, £12-18.

5.

Costume Jewellery

Once Chanel had made her mark on the fashion scene, life would never be the same again for the jewellery trade. Buttons were made from huge fake rubies, hat brims turned down with 20 carat emeralds, and Chanel models took over that ultimate badge of respectability, long strings of pearls - only now they were as large as eggs and made from fish scales and plastic. For the first time, women could buy jewellery as exciting and flamboyant as that owned by the Duchess of Windsor, but made up with good-looking chunks of glass, painted enamels and gilt instead of diamonds, precious stones and gold. And they were proud to flaunt their fakes.

COLLECTORS' NOTES

Early Paris costume jewellery from the 1930s (Chanel, Schiaparelli, etc.) is quite rare and now expensive. If you are lucky you may find an unmarked piece; look for very high-quality settings, and detail of design everywhere.

By the 1960s some of the best was being made in the United States. Trifari was only one of the manufacturers who were proud to add their names to the mould of their settings.

Any named piece of this period is good value; catalogues and advertisements in fashion magazines publicised the work of individual designers. Read them in the library for clues about the work of people or companies you like.

In the UK, a small Bond Street store called Paris House imported some of the best French pieces, particularly hair jewellery. Long hair was fashionable again, usually pinned up in chignons. Paris House sold fake tortoise-shell and gilt and jewelled pins, as well as tiaras and chunky belts of glittering metal.

Sparkle was all; stones were set in claws, so that every movement of the body would send lights radiating in every direction.

Kenneth Lane, king of English fake fashion, began his meteoric rise; Kenneth Lane was the mark on earlier pieces, Ken Lane after 1977.

1. This oval case of gilt metal has an embossed surface. The top, a huge ruby of glass, lifts up to take king-size cigarettes. American, unmarked. 1960s, £15, because it was badly rubbed. Watch out for gilt worn off in use. Cigarette cases are a social history in themselves for the collector, with the change in smoking habits.

2. The Duchess of Windsor loved jewellery and she set many fashion trends. Her animal pins and bracelets were a craze which is still active. Pavé setting, tiny stones set as close together, was characteristic of the genre; this little but exceptionally finely made dancing elephant with a ruby eye, 1960s, £25.

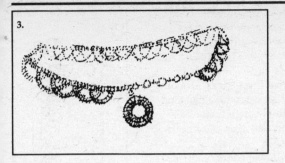

3.

4. Tiara from Paris House, made of seed pearls and tiny diamond motifs wired to a hair band.

Unfortunately at least three motifs are missing, so the value has gone way down. If you find a similar perfect one, keep it safe in tissue paper; loose pieces can be wired back. Dated 1962, marked France, £18.

3. A belt made for unisex use and worn by a male model in the John Michael Fashion Show of 1960. The ring makes it adjustable, and it was worn like a gun belt, slung low over black trousers. John Michael introduced Italian style to the men of the 1960s. Stamped "Made in France" there is not a single missing stone from the literally hundreds of claw settings. 1962, £40.

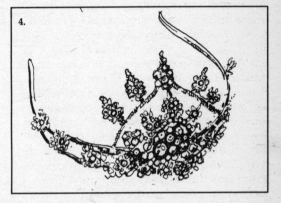

4.

5. A fantastic farrago of turquoise plastic crystals, actually knitted in a triple layer to a band of smaller crystals. This is the quintessential choker, guaranteed to stop anyone in their tracks, as it did me when I passed it on a market stall.

Not a single pendant was missing; it glittered like a pile of ice, and it sold the first day I put it out on display.

They were also made in red and in clear white, in the late 1960s. The knitted technique is unusual. French and in perfect condition, £40.

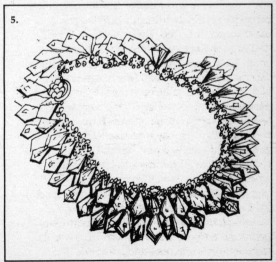

5.

Cutlery and Serving Pieces

No need to feel guilty about spending time and money on cutlery; unlike a desire for stuffed parrots, for example, friends and family agree that forks, knives and spoons are genuinely useful.

The word "cutlery" comes from an old French term for coulter, or knife-maker, who also made the blades for the plough. In general use it has come to mean utensils which are used for both preparing and eating food.

Today we have a limited number of implements; lunch knives and forks, dinner knives and forks, soup and dessert spoons, and a few extra serving pieces. But in late Victorian times, the "Family Plate Chest" in a box of polished mahogany with brass locks and handles, might contain at least two sets of carving knives and forks, an additional six kinds of spoons from egg to ice cream, fish knives, forks and servers, mustard spoons...Mrs Beeton mentions twelve kinds of spoons suitable for a "nice family of comfortable circumstances".

COLLECTORS' NOTES

This wealth of available pieces is a great boon to the collector. A first priority may be assembling an entire service of the same pattern; if you choose something like the ever-popular Fiddle, or Kings or Queens pattern, it will have been made over many decades. Concentrating on hallmarked silver is both feasible and not very expensive when you buy it piece by piece. However, for the best final value, try and keep to the same manufacturer and the same year, or at least decade. Plate is, of course, not dated but does usually have makers' marks.

There is also an assortment of less common implements to collect; strange shapes which might be asparagus tongs or pastry servers, nut picks, butter trowels, cream ladles, marrow scoops...look at printed catalogues of the period to trace their purpose. It's a glimpse of another world, both fascinating and valuable.

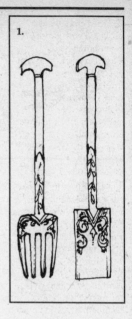

1. A delightful example of the unexpected. This set of gardener's tools, a fork and a spade, are not the miniatures I first imagined. After research, I discovered an identical illustration in a contemporary book; they are cheese servers used with a dessert service. The silver scoop cuts into the Stilton easily - the blade is unexpectedly sharp. The fork was used to balance the cheese morsel as it was lifted to your own plate.

Hallmarked silver mountings on the ivory handle and shaft give the date.

All the silver is engraved in a floriate design, and the tiny details of rivets on the handles are superb. London, 1904, £85.

2. Fitted cases were provided with almost every purchase of Victorian and Edwardian goods. Dealers used to throw away shabby cases because they looked nasty, but now customers prefer to have an original case, believing it adds authenticity. But unless the name on the case matches the contents, be wary; cases also came in standard sizes and unrelated objects can be boxed up fairly easily. A genuine case does add value; this 1910 dessert set for six as loose implements, £40. Boxed in attractive and labelled octagonal case, £75.

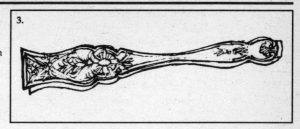

3. The asparagus season was a problem; how could you serve the floppy sticks and how could your guests eat them gracefully? Asparagus tongs, ends wide and slightly curved in, solved both difficulties. The most elegant hostess provided individual tongs for her guests and a larger server for herself. This large silver pair, beautifully engraved in 1872, £85.

4. Preserve spoons usually have wide bowls, often slightly lobed as here, but always a little deeper in order to carry enough marmalade or jam to your toast. Unlike the remade berry and sifter spoons, these smaller forms have seldom been faked up to now. Look for a firm, strong join between handle and bow - that is where damage occurs. 1825, £55.

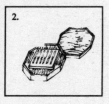

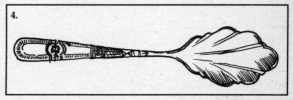

5. Carved bread knives offer interest and variety at a very modest price. Most date from the 1870s to the 1940s. The motifs include wheat, corn, flowers, mottos; there were also ivory and horn handles. Engraved blades are an added attraction. Watch out for split handles - they can be hard to see in heavy carving. Loose tangs are easier to repair.

According to motif and material, £18-28.

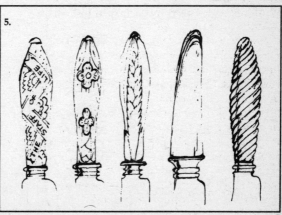

Decanters

These delightful collectables developed out of necessity; barrelled beer and wine had to be drawn into smaller containers. Subsequent pouring into a glass also left behind any dregs. By 1715, the definition of "Decanter - a clear bottle for the holding of wine to be poured into glasses" was established.

COLLECTORS' NOTES

Most decanters are glass to allow you to see the clarity of the liquid and its colour. That was an important asset when poison often came dissolved in the wine. It's also easy to clean!

Early decanters usually had handles; new shapes, mainly without them, became popular around 1720, although claret jugs have kept their handles, as well as their pouring spouts to this day. Glass stoppers replaced corks; the shaft was ground inside to ensure a close fit.

Designs of the past two centuries range so widely that it is impossible to date a decanter by shape alone. Glass is seldom marked, so the colour and quality of the glass is as important as the decoration (see p. 78).

Silver stands or mounts may help dating, but they can also conceal damage. Check inside the rim for chips or cracks. Watch out for chips off all cut edges, hard to see at first.

1. The more elaborate 18th century decanters were expensive even at the time, but by the end of the century there was a reasonably generous supply, and many fine late Georgian decanters can be found under £100. Below, the practical "shaft and globe" design still popular today; its stability is always an attractive visual feature. The similar ship's decanters have a larger flat base. 1790s, £45.

2. From c.1780, rings were cut around the tall shafts for easy handling and extra decoration. Below, a decanter with three neck rings in angled facets over a sturdy swelling base, with mushroom stopper. Different factories had favourite cutting patterns on the neck rings, see left. C.1810, Cork, £85.

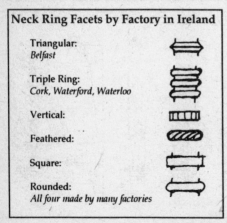

Neck Ring Facets by Factory in Ireland	
Triangular: *Belfast*	
Triple Ring: *Cork, Waterford, Waterloo*	
Vertical:	
Feathered:	
Square:	
Rounded: *All four made by many factories*	

3. Lots of sparkle was soon required on glowing mahogany tables. In this square spirit decanter, every possible surface was embellished; vertical ribs were alternatively left clear or cut flat with tiny hatch cuttings. A sign of quality is that the ribs of hatching are exactly matched on the round stopper and even under the base where it vanishes into the central point. Even the short neck has its step ribs, cut round to match the base. A little miracle from 1790 and very reasonable at £85.

4. This blown and moulded decanter was a standard of the 1840s on. In this case it is made especially nice by a blown and ribbed stopper and a little kick to the base. Genuinely matching stoppers are an important requirement. £55.

5. After the 1851 Great Exhibition, a riot of colour and design took over. Glass became ruby red and swirly yellow, forest green and even purple, overlaid and etched, or painted and enamelled. Fine examples of the period, once despised for not being Georgian and vulgarly flashy to boot, are eagerly sought today. However, you may find a more modest version with considerable potential. Avoid faded or worn gilding which leaves behind a white shadow trail. Unless a very un-usual piece, it's worse than no decoration. Acid-etched engraving lasts longer and is more attractive. This 1870s example shows its age by its ruby colour and the fern pattern so beloved of the gardening Victorians at that time. £90.

6. Art Deco at its very, very best. Look for that distinctive enamel geometric decoration, usually black or red on very heavy, glittering lead crystal. Some, like this one, have the added attraction of that popular motif, a rising sun. If you are lucky and find one, be prepared to pay £100. Possibly Czechoslovakian.

7. Later 20th century decanters are still under-valued. This 1920s slim shape, like a cocktail shaker, is in cut glass of Vaseline green; unusual enough to cost £97 now. Look out for fashionable Art Deco colours and high styled decoration.

Dolls and Doll Accessories

Our interest in human beings is probably at the root of the preoccupation that many people have with dolls and doll accessories. Over the entire history of society, as far back as we can tell, there were dolls for children to play with and probably for adults to regard as something special. Certainly dolls play a part in many religious rituals and very occasionally they can become a symbol of evil or possession.

Happily, most of our dolls are very domestic indeed, and most doll collectors regard them with affection, like children. Others are fascinated by their reflection of social life - and for them there are dolls dressed for every social occasion, from babyhood to fashion shows. Even quite new dolls can reach high prices and rare ones are extremely expensive, but there are enough still around for the modest and motivated buyer to build up a considerable collection of interesting small people.

COLLECTORS' NOTES

Early dolls are way out of our price range, unless you strike very lucky at a house clearance sale where a family is selling off their belongings. For detailed information on what to look for, make use of the reading list which begins on p. 190.

Often, early dolls are not playthings at all, but fashion or costume plates. They have quite grown-up faces, relatively slim bodies and often hair set in a chignon or other style which cannot be rearranged. A recent sale of an 1870s' doll reached £25,000. 1920s' and 1930s' dolls dressed in the latest fashion are often called boudoir dolls, as it was considered chic to have a pile of them in your boudoir or on the bed.

Not all adult dolls are expensive; during the 1940s and 1950s and the formation of the United Nations there was a great vogue for dolls dressed in national costumes. Good examples, with well-made clothes and detailed accessories are well worth collecting as they are now becoming quite scarce.

1.

1. A rather grown-up doll of the 1915 period, in its original muslin dress. £80. Doll collecting has become so specialised that any new entrant must spend some time in reading and looking at auctions and museums before attempting to start an informed collection.

Most of the valuable dolls are French or German, made from the mid-19th century on. Marked examples of particularly desirable models from Jumeau, Kestner or Simon and Halbig have reached staggering prices - not just hundreds but thousands. However, unmarked and English dolls in general are more affordable; look for period clothes and good condition underneath. Modern copies are usually "Victorian", and very clean.

2.

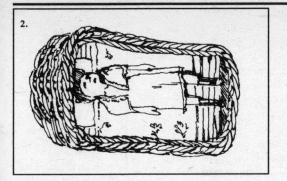

3.

2. A doll in its cradle, probably turn of the century, and in a home-made dress and hand-knitted sweater. Together they will sell around £65-75. If a doll is in its original box, it will add to the current price, although the child who was not allowed to play with it may not think it a fair exchange.

4. Cut-out dolls and their clothes are part of the new collectors' market. Once sold in huge quantities and with every possible outfit, these glimpses of the 1940s and 1950s have all but disappeared, so those that remain are eminently collectable. From £15 for a very basic set to £95 for the dress in the New Look by Dior. Many of the faces and the outfits were based on Hollywood stars - Judy Garland paper cut-outs from *Meet Me In St Louis* were very popular with parents, and even Scarlett O'Hara in *Gone With The Wind* had her green velvet dress translated into paper.

3. Kewpie dolls of celluloid were in demand at all amusement parks and state fairs in America. They were made in the 1930s and 1940s; in their box or as special models they can be priced in the hundreds, but this standard model baby with no clothes was £45.

5. Even Barbie is getting into the act. There's an active collectors' market and a book for the early models; this c.1970, £55.

4.

5.

Dolls and Doll Accessories

As much as we love the miniature aspect of dolls being small people, their accessories seem even more amusing and delightful. For every searcher after bisque heads and jointed rags, there are ten who yearn to furnish a complete doll's house with tiny candlesticks, a minute kitchen stove and needlepoint rugs on the floor.

COLLECTORS' NOTES

Most doll's house furniture is larger than you might imagine - and so are the doll people to go with them. Tiny silver or ceramic furnishings are often miniatures for adults to display on shelves or tables. But there is no reason why, if the scale is right, they can't be put to better use.

Doll's houses now are extremely expensive, even damaged or commercially made houses of fold-out paper or plywood, produced during the 1920s or 1930s. You may be lucky and find a home-made model - I saw a Tudor Inn at a local Suffolk auction which sold for £90 - but they are likely to be crudely made. For an elegant house, buy a kit, paper and paint it for the period you prefer, and in fifty years it will be an heirloom!

Furniture is also soaring in price. But single pieces, without boxes or labels, can still be found. I bought two silver miniatures for £50, a Chippendale chair and table, hallmarked 1921.

Ivory carved pieces from India, dated late 19th century, are also available from about £60 up. And 1920s and 1930s pieces of contemporary style are still nowhere near as popular with decorators, and therefore nowhere near the price, of earlier models.

Because the prices are so high, most dealers can reognise German and American tin furniture of the late 19th century, made with printed transfers on basic pressed-tin plate. Reproductions have started coming on the market; unfortunately for the customer, old rust and new rust look alike.

The skills of model-making are rare, but there are a few craftsmen making interesting pieces. If you see some of good quality, buy it, age or no.

1. A tiny glass decanter of minute proportions and exquisite cutting. Late 19th century, bought from a glass dealer, hence the reasonable price of £45. Look for clear glass and the sharp edges of hand cutting - pressed glass doll's tableware was turned out in quantity as late as the 1950s and1960s in the cheapest colours of pink, blue and yellow, just like plastic ones of the same period; neither are much collected. Yet. When you try a new area, read up about the makers and the names of their products.

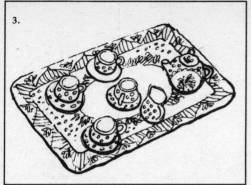

3.

4.

4. A tin tray with a floral design on a black ground. It once had a little stand - you can see the lugs on the back, but that has gone. 1890s-1910, £65.

3. A complete tea service, the tray only 5 or 6 cm long. The cups and saucers are finely made, with a turquoise band of enamel decoration. The tray has a centre floral cartouche; at one time there were gilded initials on it, because the white lines which faded gilding leaves are still discernible. C.1925.

In spite of its Western appearance, the thin porcelain, slightly blue, is probably Japanese; there are no marks. During the 1920s and 1930s, Japan sent huge cargoes of porcelain trinkets to the West which diminished their reputation. Sometimes it is marked with "Japan", sometimes with the name of the manufacturer and later with "Foreign" to avoid anti-Japanese feeling.

Czechoslovakia was another source of porcelain novelties during the same period, although the potting is not as fine.

5. A most desirable pram. Of black leatherette, it would have been the latest style in 1910. Watch out for bare patches on corners and in the folds of the hood, and rusty fittings. Make sure the wheels match. £75-95.

2. A miniature sink with its tiled back; were it not for the water heater and the taps it could fit into a late Victorian home, but the real enthusiast will know that period is everything. Of wood and ceramic, 1920s, and about £40. The 1920s period is not as well regarded as the Victorians, giving the budget collector a chance to start a new collection at a reasonable price. Keep the same standards as you would for adult objects; look for high style or period pointers like the water heater and taps.

5.

Embroidery

The design, preparation and execution of embroidery is one of the greatest tranquillisers known to the world. In the antique world, a woman like Penelope was considered the ideal wife - content to be useful and ornamental at the same time. In mediaeval society, as spinning became industrialised, the embroiderer became idealised in the same way; Henry II granted tax-free status for life to the woman who taught his daughters gold needlework.

Unfortunately the Inland Revenue no longer confers on us the same status, but embroidery is still the comfort and delight of many. Its pleasures are not confined to women, because there are many men who not only design embroidery but who work it themselves. And both men and women enjoy collecting embroidery of the past.

COLLECTORS' NOTES

Most early embroidery is now quite rare and expensive, which makes Victorian examples about the oldest that would come into our price bracket.

Look for the varied designs of the last half of the century; in the 1880s, woolwork and silk embroidery was very popular and there are surprising numbers of pincushions, purses and even footstools around, although the latter, being usually substantial in size, may be over our limit. I did see one at a recent market for only £40, a lovely turquoise background with a typical floral centre. Check the edges of all needlework very carefully - that's where it tends to pull away from the frame or border.

Beadwork is very Victorian. Examine it carefully; sometimes a tiny loose thread will let half a dozen beads fall away. Visit a bead specialist before you try and repair the break with modern beads; you can buy old ones which will look much more appropriate. And keep every single bead yourself for the best repairs.

1. Ladies in front of the fire used these small screens to hold up and shield their delicate complexions. I always thought it was far too likely that the fabric would catch fire, but perhaps that is being too cynical. In any case, they were mounted, like this one, c.1870, with the most delicate embroidery, here in purple and yellowsilks with a design of a green bird in the middle.

The frame is in simple pine instead of mahogany, oak or walnut, so that accounts for the reasonable price of £55.

With fringed pieces, check around the edges very carefully - they often pull away or become very tatty, giving the whole piece a rather rat-tail look.

2.

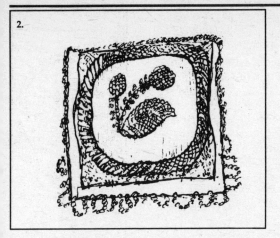

2. This tiny pincushion is embroidered with a wild-flower design in yellow and green chenille. The background in brown is fringed with blue and green twisted scallops.

The wool has become quite dirty, but cleaning must be undertaken with very great care. The threads are almost certainly weakened with age and dirt, and will be liable to break under the slightest stress. You can use a dry-cleaning fluid on a pad, but handle it as if it were glass! C.1865, £25.

3.

3. A little beaded bag, with a metal clasp. This one was made by hand, for it has the initials of its owner or maker cunningly worked into the design.

Beaded bags were made in so many designs that it is almost impossible to duplicate one. They have begun to rise in price.

This very pretty one, embroidered with 1890, and with its original clasp, £65. However, you can buy 1930s bags for a quite a bit less, and build up a collection which will be very valuable in just a few years.

4. Typical steel engraving of the period which was used to make a pattern for embroidery. I found a large traycloth with the original design, a real treat. £95 for the pair.

4.

Embroidery

The beginning of this century was a transition period for the needleworker. Young students were taught by Jessie Newbery at the Glasgow School of Art, whose own work was strongly affected by Art Nouveau, and her assistant Anne Macbeth, younger and more aware of bold Art Deco shapes, and who was to have considerable influence on the Royal School of Needlework until her death in 1948.

Both women loved appliqué, and their bold leaf and flower designs are distinctive, but much copied by their students and others. Anne Macbeth was particularly interested in getting everyone to do their own designing, a goal still valid today for teachers.

From the 1950s onwards, there have been constant revivals; Jacobean crewel work briefly in the 1960s, patchwork, heavily in debt to the American passion for it, and wool canvas work from the 1970s on, with the rise in preprinted kits for decorative home projects. The result has been hand-made, mass-production of reproduction pieces; bewildering for the new collector.

COLLECTORS' NOTES

For real investment value, look especially for good and original designs. Much contemporary work has been based on copying older pieces. The Royal School of Needlework has good records for research into the creation and history of particular designs, and although it won't tell you the actual worker of your piece, unless it's unique, it will help to confirm its probable date.

Skilled needlework is an advantage - naive charm can't always overcome botched sewing. At least, not until it becomes folk art!

The work of well-known contemporary designers is expensive, but there's a wealth of fresh ideas and unusual materials coming out of craft fairs and shops. Hand-made pieces often find their way into the antiques trade. If tempted, be rigorous about quality, even on a budget. It has no substitute.

1. A typical north country rug; naive bold subject and bright colours, now faded to subtle greys and beige. Made for the farmhouse, rugs like this are not expensive, just difficult to find. Look for simple stitches, and a stained canvas back, from decades of use on the hearth or passage. Modern copies (seldom intentional fakes) will be very clean. C.1910, £50.

2. A 1920s stitched towel; a similar naive pattern, but inhibited by conventional ideas about pretty colours. Every suburban house would have at least one set. Though limited as art, it immediately brings the room and its inhabitants to life, at very little cost. £4.

3.

3. A magnificent shawl of the 1930s, its Chinese-influenced design embroidered in brilliant colours of blue and green on a deep yellow background of silk. There are touches of brick red on the flowers.

For some reason anonymous shawls of this period have not yet reached the high levels of Paisleys and others. Search now for the best examples with designs that reflect the period. This geometric rendering of an oriental pattern on thin silk is the perfect find; typical in its colouring and design, completely undamaged, and the embroidery is of very fine workmanship.

Check fringing carefully for pulled sections. £78.

4. Beige tape, scrolled and machine-sewn onto pinky-beige artificial silk. This small 1920s traycloth design is a reflection of old crewel work, but in paler 1930s colours. Traycloths were never in a silky fabric because they had to be washed so often, but the introduction of rayon changed all that. A period piece at only £4-7.

4.

5. Personal articles have given way almost entirely to work for the home. Canvas, wool and the simple tent stitch provide pleasure for thousands and possibilities for tomorrow's collector. Look for unusual ideas like this navy and red pelmet with its clever zig-zag base. 1970s, £28.

5.

Fireplace Furniture

Room heating came from open coal fires until well into the 1930s. The average household, particularly in the country or smaller village, still had a fire in every room, just as Regency and Victorian families had had. In most districts, wood was too valuable to burn but coal was cheap and reliable, with a warming glow.

And by the fire, there was an assortment of buckets, carriers, baskets, tongs, pokers, brushes and fenders of almost limitless design. Because of their durability and weight, a surprising number of these are still around, but collectors with space to buy more than one of these large pieces are rare; most should be called buyers rather than collectors, equipping their homes with period accessories. If that applies to you, there are now two or three books in print which will help to find an appropriate style for your rooms.

COLLECTORS' NOTES

Working tools are made of wrought iron for extra strength and flexibility, although fenders are cast. Handles could be cast brass or polished iron; some were silver plate, and some from the Arts and Crafts or Art Nouveau periods are copper.

Kitchen and country tools hung on the wall, but in drawing rooms and bedrooms a small stand and coal box would be at the hearth, the box refilled every morning and evening. A screen hid the empty grate in the summer.

A complete stand held a brush, a poker, a shovel and a pair of tongs. In the more elegant homes handles would match finials on a fender, although the coal box might be quite separate. A small rack to support the poker or tongs while you were remaking the fire was often included. Stands which have lost their accessories are often mistaken for umbrella stands. You can assemble a matching, or at least a near-matching, set with a little time and patience.

Coal boxes were disguised as what-nots, desks, bookcases, or cushioned seats. Only the metal-lined interior gives them away.

1. Mid-Victorian cast-iron box with painted slip-in front panel, white ceramic casters and shovel, handle slightly chipped. There is no rust inside or out, the interior is complete with its lining. C.1850, £70. If the panel were of finer quality painting, then £90 or more. Panels were often replaced when they had become too dirty to be cleaned any more.

2. An Edwardian coal box with lift-up door and inset pewter handle. The shovel was kept inside and this one has been lost. Made of golden oak, this is a cheaper model than the iron example above, and without casters. Very heavy when full, it has also lost its lining. £18-20.

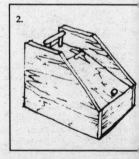

3. Complete set on a matching stand. The body of the stand is brass, as are the handles and the entire shaft of the shovel and brush. Alternative styles of the same late 1800s period are shown on the side. Be careful of lacquered brass, which is likely to mean a reproduction never intended for serious use.

A well-used poker may be slightly distorted, as would be the tongs. There may be some wear on the handles, although that is less likely.

Bright clean shovels are a giveaway, though; they marked very quickly, and years of coal dust piling up into corners is difficult to fake.

The hairs on the brush would be bristle until after 1950.

Sets were made in large numbers so it should be relatively easy to find a set or at least related designs. Anything with an unusual handle might be more difficult to match. C.1885, £90-120 for a full set in reasonable condition. This one, £92.

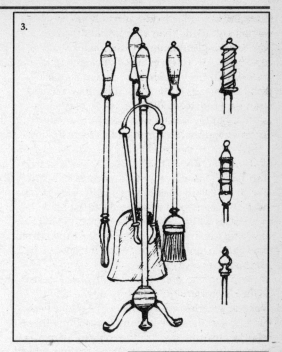

3.

4. Matching poker rest for the set, found at a different fair some three years later. Often mistaken for shoe or boot scrapers, they stood inside the fender on one side to save putting the dusty tool back on its rack. On its own, £12.

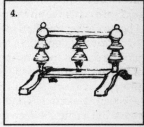

4.

5. Matching fender in brass, on iron base. £70-90 or more, depending on size. Club fenders had leather seats; in demand now, they are very expensive. Cast-iron bedroom fenders for small fireplaces cost from £25. In copper Art Nouveau style, £60 up, depending on size.

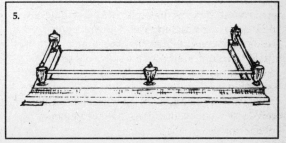

5.

Garden Ornaments

Ranging from plaster gnomes to Roman marble temples, garden ornaments are now big business. Older examples, because of their weight and general inconvenience, are seldom shown at indoor fairs or one-day markets. Go to house clearances, auctions and architectural salvage companies instead. There are a few specialist shops, but these usually concentrate on the grander and more expensive ornaments.

COLLECTORS' NOTES

Browsing for the heavy stuff requires a slightly different technique; look down and sideways, as well as in corners, and along the tops of old bookcases where bits of stone statues get left.

Search for an attractive shape rather than detail; most of the time you'll be seeing it from twenty or thirty feet away.

Don't confuse stone with fragile plaster casts, which Victorians thought very intellectual to have in libraries, etc. A little gentle stroke with your fingertip is an easy way to recognise the rougher texture of stone, the coldness of marble, or the ultra-smoothness of plaster casting, which of course is not weatherproof.

Be inventive - random pieces of gates, fences or signs made of decorative ironwork can be re-used as screens indoors, or simply hung on the wall. Keep them dry and coat with a rust preventative.

Stoneware is often found covered in lichen and moss. In fact, new stoneware is sometimes artificially coated with yogurt or some such substance to get the growth started. When removed it can leave ugly patches of staining, so it's best to take anything valuable to a stone restorer, or consult them about cleaning.

Old terracotta seed pots are now sold from many kitchen gardens of the big houses. They are generally taller and narrower than our modern pots, and they rise straight up with no double rims. Use them by all means, but keep them out of the frost.

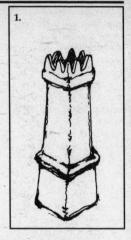

1.

1. Chimney pots are one of the great recycling successes of the decade. Without the influence of garden designers, they would have been torn off old houses and pounded into rubble. Now the contractor will head for the nearest architectural salvage company with his load of treasures.

Many are regional; northern towns were full of fanciful tops like these pointed crowns from Manchester. Others are basic with just a rounded top edge roll.

Look out for cracks, either from fires or from careless removal.

Since they have no bottoms they make perfect planters where you need a long, free root run.

Once free to anyone near a demolition site, now cleaned and wirebrushed to remove soot, £80-120.

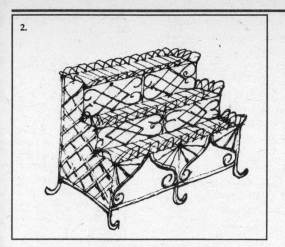

2. Original wirework plant stands are still around in quite large quantities and at reasonable cost. But restoration can be very unnerving - scrape away the rust and you may not have anything left. They are really only suited to conservatories - true also of most old garden furniture. In the past, servants moved these in and out as required; will you be as vigilant?

Check that all the little decorative edging circles are there; it's quite hard to see a few missing ones when you are looking at the whole stand.

There are new reproduction stands now in similar patterns, but they are easy to spot as all the wirework is neat and tidy, the paint is fresh and there's no rust!

This green stand is relatively clean and still sturdy enough to hold a good collection of plants. C.1870, £96.

3. A sundial, still the perfect focal point for a garden path. Most will be far too expensive for our budget, but there are simpler and later versions, still with some age. This classic pedestal, probably reproduction sixty years ago, has a home-made gnomon of glazed ceramic. which made it special - and just affordable. 1930s, £99.

Other sundials are just a dial, to hang on a wall.

4. A set of ceramic units by Doulton's made throughout the 1880s. They are individual flower pots or pot-holders which could be combined to make up any length of planter, either for the window sill or for a conservatory. Watch out for cracks which could split the pots during a frost, or keep them safely in a frost-free place. Crazing inside is not too bad, as long as it doesn't look deep. This wonderful find, in dark blue majolica with moulded figures of mediaeval gardeners, was seven pots long, but of course they could come in any number. £65.

Glass

Glass is one of the most remarkable substances ever invented. Natural glass, as lava flow, comes from the earth's kiln, but the story of glass-making is still a mystery. Somewhere, probably in Mesopotamia, and sometime, probably around 2,000BC, a craftsman discovered that melted silica, soda and lime will cool to a hard, translucent substance. It would be another 2,000 years before blown glass was invented, again in the Middle East, around 100BC. It was blown glass that changed a minor art form to a major, irreplaceable ingredient of everyday life. And yet it remains a mystery, a substance which is not a solid, but a liquid in suspension.

COLLECTORS' NOTES

The Romans built glasshouses for common wares in nearly all their colonies; more elegant products were imported from home. Authentic examples now cost well over £100.

All early glass was made with soda and lime; it is surprisingly light. Iridescence is no guarantee of age. There are many ways to create the effect, and tourist souvenirs from the Middle East can be sold as ancient pieces. But mediaeval glass is scarcer than Roman, and seldom offered for sale. Old hot-glass motifs are still being used - blobs called prunts and trailing threads - so it's easy to be fooled until you know more.

From the island of Murano, Venetian glassmakers dominated the world trade from the Renaissance to the 18th century. A 16th century tazza will cost hundreds, even thousands, of pounds. Even 19th century copies are expensive.

English and Irish glass, first blown plain and then decorated with cutting, dominated the 18th century. Lead glass had been developed in London - heavy, durable and with a deep texture which was perfect for engraving and cutting. Although fine drinking glasses from the first part of the 18th century are now £300-600, late 18th century cut glass jugs and decanters are widely available within our budget.

1. This Irish decanter dates from approximately 1770. The rings on the neck suggest it was made in Belfast (see Decanters). Look for clear glass, with few imperfections and a kind of oily surface - a sign of the best lead crystal. £75-90. 18th century glass varies greatly in colour; the finest will have just a touch of grey, the thinner ones may be yellowy. Very clear, bright glass without any imperfections is 20th century reproduction.

2. These dwarf ale glasses are early 18th century, although they were made later as well. Sometimes described as syllabub or jelly glasses, strong ale might have been served in them, or sweet dessert wines.

Ales come in such a bewildering array of bowls and bases that you can build up a delightful harlequin set quite quickly.

On the left is a wrythen, or twisted bowl over a moulded knop; the centre ale has a heavier base, and the octagonal bowl has no stem at all. Engraved designs are particularly prized, and condition must be perfect.1760-90, £55-85. The foot of an 18th century glass is always wider than its bowl, often with a narrow folded rim to protect the edge. Many genuinely early glasses have had their feet cut down, which destroys their value.

3. If you love the colour of blue glass but most examples are way beyond your price range, why not collect liners? They were made for silver serving pieces, to keep the food from tarnishing the metal, and especially for salt cellars. There are two salt liners, one round and one square, in the group above.

All sorts of other dishes had liners as well, and some, like the lovely lobed dish, are spectacularly beautiful on their own. £10-35.

Not all liners are blue - there are amethyst, green and purple examples, too.

They are hard to date; I believe these are 18th century because of the colour, and the slight imperfections. Also, the shapes they would have fitted are appropriate for that period.

If you have dishes that need liners, they can be replaced to order.

4. Fashions in collecting change. In the 1950s only a few serious collectors were really interested in early 18th century English glass; then for a while balusters and sweetmeats, especially engraved ones, became extremely popular, with lectures on decoration and colour-twist stems. Now we are beginning to appreciate later 18th century and 19th century tableware.

This delightful small wine glass dates from about 1790-1820. The ultra-slim stem has a faceted knop and the narrow bowl is wheel-engraved with a complex design. Forty years ago, it would have been called late Georgian and sold for £150. Twenty years ago, it would have been called early Victorian, and sold for £20 and today, properly dated, it should sell for about £90 as a single, £240 for a pair.

Glass

With the 1851 Exhibition, coloured glass from Bohemia became the rage, and soon American factories in particular became the leaders in the strange shaded mixtures and experimental colours we associate with Victorian glass. Engraving techniques with acid replaced hand work, and suddenly glass followed the fashion of the day into mass-production.

COLLECTORS' NOTES

The excitement of 19th century coloured glass can only be imagined; it was as if every flower in the garden burst into bloom at the same time. Patterns followed fashion, from the pie-crust frills of Victorian design to the natural harmonies of Arts and Crafts.

Earlier glassmakers left their rough pontil mark under the domed foot. During the 19th century the pontil marks were ground down to a flat foot, which helps to date the glass. The foot was smaller, too, and often cut underneath in a star.

For the first time, pressed glass began to rival blown glass for the middle of the market. Although American factories produced the most innovative designs and techniques, examples of their best work are seldom available in this country, which makes collecting very frustrating. But there are many pleasant patterns which were developed here, and to make things a little easier, many pressed glass factories marked their wares, an unusual asset to the collector of glassware.

Look for the most famous of all, the Sowerby peacock mark, and others - Greener's, Davidson, and many factories in Newcastle.

Although the American factories produced the most magnificent range of tableware in pressed glass patterns, eagerly collected now, English 19th century glasshouses making pressed glass concentrated on coloured and marbled novelties - vases, spill vases, boxes, trinkets etc. A few produced clear glass in imitation of cut glass originals, less interesting and rather tame.

1. At the beginning of the 19th century, cut glass was still pre-eminent. When the Glass Tax in England was abolished in 1830, competition became intense. For a while tradition succeeded with heavier, deeper and more brilliant pieces like this remarkable egg cup, one of six, that would dazzle any breakfaster; c.1815, £60 for the set.

2.

3.

1.

2. This water or lemonade jug shows the lighter styles of mid-century. The elaborate cutting is confined to the top and a star on the base. Simple flutes on the body emphasise the shape without obscuring the contents. C.1840, £48.

If there is a cut motif along the rim, examine the edges very carefully. It is very hard to see chips, but they will lower the value considerably.

3. A basket vase, the peacock mark of Sowerby's on the base. Sowerby's is best known for its small pieces with clever moulding and good, clear colours in plain and marbled patterns.

Diamond and basket-weave surface textures were combined with moulded handles, and other ornamentation; some were quite elaborate.

The collector of 19th century glass has the benefit of factory records to help dating. C.1860, £35.

4. After the 1851 Exhibition in London rounded shapes, curves and rainbows of colour took over every household.

This pretty deep blue vase, painted with flowers and lightly gilded, is a restrained example.

Watch out for faded painting and gilding on top of the glass. It was often only cold-glazed without being put into the kiln, and it can rub off very easily. Little jewelled drops break off, too, and that will take up to half off the valuation. Bohemia, £66.

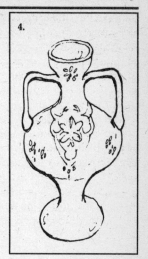

4.

5. By the end of the century clear glass returned in classic styles, and decoration became linked to natural forms and eventually to Art Nouveau. This butter dish was engraved with ferns, another Victorian pre-occupation in the 1880s. That helps to date it; £35.

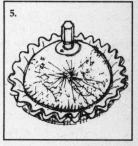

5.

6. Yellow marbled glass in a gentle curve, needing only a single band of gilded wriggle decoration to set it off. The handle is thicker at the bottom, where it was first attached and then pulled up and stuck on the top, getting thinner. This generally means a date after 1860; handles thicker at the top are usually earlier. This came with four glasses, one badly worn; always check *everything* in a set. C.1880, £80 the set.

6.

Glass

Glass in the 20th century has met strong stylistic demands from Art Nouveau and Art Deco, the later Scandinavian influence with its chunky and monumental cubes of clear and frosted glass, and at present a rather haphazard mixture of modern studio glass and individual talents.

Learning about this century is easier in one way - the pieces are often signed, and exhibitions of studio glassmakers are held regularly - but understanding what forms it may be a little more difficult. More expertise is required of the collector to sort out the new classics from the fashionable junk. You need to develop a feel for the material and its possibilities which will help you through the minefield of contemporary taste to a fine collection for the future.

COLLECTORS' NOTES

Visit a large, commercial glasshouse - many have open days or will allow you in by appointment. The experience is quite extraordinary, and many of the technical terms which are hard to understand in writing will be instantly clear.

Once you appreciate the basic techniques, find a local studio glasshouse where you can see artists working on individual pieces of art glass. You'll never look at a drinking glass or vase in the same way again.

Glass collecting is an elusive art; you need to look, handle, and look again. Study examples of the kind of style and period you like and would want to collect. Art Nouveau glass has reached ridiculous heights, and the famous names of Gallé, Daum and Tiffany are known even in the smallest market. Art Deco glass is less appreciated, and there are chances there for the observant collector to find unrecognised fine pieces. Scandinavian glass is still described as contemporary, but Orrefors dates from 1914.

Signed Italian glass of the 1950s is suddenly bringing large sums at auction, and it was sold from the shelves of department stores not so long ago. Look around today for tomorrow's classics!

1. Art Nouveau found its perfect partner in the fluid curves of blown glass which could take on iridescent colours and natural forms with an ease no other material could match.

French and German glass from houses like Gallé, Daum, and Loetz, will be over our budget, but there are good examples of the style in smaller pieces or in those blown anonymously in any one of the studios.

Study named pieces in museums and auction houses to develop a feel for the period. Then you might find a vase like this, c.1910, £55.

Look for flowing lines and rich, deep colours which blend into each other and change under different lights.

2.

2. Art Deco wasn't sympathetic to free-blown glass, but pieces like this can be found with all the characteristics of the period; a flat surface, linear, acid-etched design on peach marbled glass, and best of all, a chrome base. 1930s, £45.

4.

4. Bold, bright enamelled design on clear glass is another 1920s signal to look for; this jam jar with typical squared knob, £35.

3. A great virtue of the Art Deco period is its sense of humour. Arts and Crafts and Art Nouveau artists took themselves very seriously. But the roaring twenties managed to produce lots of good cheer - look for that light-hearted element in design, as in this cocktail shaker of white glass, enamelled with a crowing cock in yellow and red. 1920s, £95. The decanter on p. 65 from the same period has the slick narrow shape and the wild colour but none of the lightness and joy.

5. Scandinavian influence on British homes began quite early. Orrefors, one the most famous houses, began producing art glass in 1913. Although much of their most famous work is above our budget, they also produced attractive household pieces which are markedly less costly, and now becoming rare themselves and very desirable. This wine bucket is marked. C.1950s, £85. Look for simplified shapes, heavy, clear glass, usually colourless, and little or no decoration.

6. There are dozens of new designers and glass-blowers making individual pieces of studio glass. Anyone seriously interested should go to the Craft Council who keep illustrations and records of the various artists.

Sam Herman, an American who came to London many years ago, is prized as a pioneer in studio glass, and for his imaginative and innovative design which continues to evolve. Some of his early pieces now reach auction; this tiny bottle, c.1975, £75.

3.

5.

6.

Glass

Glass has a long history of surprises. First, because of its ability to take on almost any form or shape, no matter how fantastic, and then because it is such an adaptable medium for imitation.

Even before blown glass was invented, tinted and marbled blocks were carved into bowls and sent as presents from the Middle East to the Emperors of China. Jade and turquoise were, after all, quite common, but glass was unique! On a strict budget we may not rival the gifts of Asia, but there are delightful glass objects which seem to fall into no obvious category, but which provide the collector with interest and pleasure.

COLLECTORS' NOTES

Some surprising objects are made in glass. I have seen little glass boxes which could be stone, porcelain plates which are milk glass, chunky jet bookends of black glass, striated agate paper-openers of glass, and just to turn the tables, the occasional transparent cup or carved shell which turns out not to be glass but rock crystal.

Identifying glass is usually easy once you pick it up; it is always cold to the touch. But take care in lifting any piece, no matter how solid it looks. Glass can be so fragile that a sharp fingernail can shatter a bowl; I have also known a piece of pressed glass to bounce off a wooden floor, but please don't try.

Each kind of object offers a lesson in how that particular effect was made, and often why glass was chosen to create it in the first place.

The bulb glasses are a perfect example. Most of the ones we see around are from about 1880 to 1920. Their tops can be fluted and rippled, the rounded bases plain or gilded and flowered. But they were not designed primarily for decoration; Victorians were mad about nature, and fascinated by growing things. Bulbs could show off their root systems in the glass while the hyacinth above perfumed the room. Be a glass collector and learn about the world.

1. Bulb glasses for growing hyacinths indoors occur in such lovely colours and variety that a collection can be quickly assembled - wonderful when empty and even better filled with blooming flowers.

Early examples are rare, but towards 1850 they become fairly common. There were a number of classic shapes - the tall thin tube that spreads out at the base to accommodate the roots, the round-bellied Victorian favourite like a little posy glass, and 1920s glasses like this amber one below in a rippled glass.

Identification is simple; the top must curve out sharply out to make a cup for the bulb. The cup can be simple or fluted or frilled. From £18-60, depending on colour and decoration. A group in the window would make a grand show.

1.

2.

2. When workmen finished at the end of the day, the molten glass left in the melting pot was considered their property. They made utensils for their homes and ornaments for gifts or to sell. Traditionally called friggers or "end-of-day" glass, they include small jugs, hats, rolling pins, bells, ships and even walking sticks, all of which collectors covet.

Today, they are easily copied, or wrongly attributed to Nailsea, famous for its flecked and filigree glass. This little hat of yellow-flecked blue glass is late 19th century, and too thick to be Nailsea, £25-30.

3.

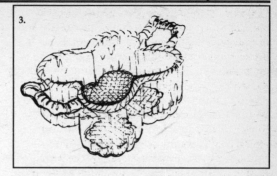

3. A pressed glass dish, unusually deep - until I discovered it was the holder from a cruet set. Now I have to find the bottles. 1910, £12 alone, £45 complete.

4. A fascinating relic of the past; once a pub in Cumberland was filled with three dozen of these great glass dispensers; now you are lucky to find one anywhere. Only the tap is bronze.

In spite of its northern home throughout the 1930s, this was made in Soho, London. And according to the gilt lettering, it was meant to be filled with Scotch whisky. Glass can't get more intra-regional than that! C.1910, £85.

4.

The roar CHIEL

5.

5. Not so unusual as an object, this little scent bottle is a copy of Venetian glass, with its white filigree swirl on a ruby-red base. The metal cap and chain is silver gilt, but the real surprise is in the manufacturer's label; it was made in Russia c.1850 during their great expansion into the glass trade. £95, for its rarity value as well.

Gloves, Hats and Handbags

Personal belongings are like fashion - a season or two after they are bought, they seem dowdy and old-fashioned. Then, after a while, you begin to be curious about what they were like; forty years on, fashion has swung back into admiring either the material, the design or the style.

Gloves and hats have suffered most from this natural cycle. During the past decades, perhaps for the first time in centuries, both have been allowed to drift off society's "required" list. Women today wear hats only on very special occasions, although gloves are still in evidence during the winter - sensible, boring and plain.

This makes old-fashioned gloves and hats, smelling faintly of scented lavender, even more of a find. Make sure you open up those round and rectangular boxes at markets and fairs.

COLLECTORS' NOTES

Look for single gloves as well as pairs; elaborate gloves of the Renaissance are found only in museum displays, but there are often individually embroidered gloves from c.1860 on, surviving somehow without their partner in the forlorn hope of reunion, and these are not usually very expensive.

Many of the finest were made in France; that includes short white gloves in kid, lace or crochet and cotton piqué, worn during the summer by respectable ladies.

Look for glove and hat accessories, too. Glove stretchers were a necessity when kid gloves would have to be opened up every time they were put on. Stretchers were made in bone, ivory and more economically in wood. Even as late as the 1920s, glove boxes included a little elastic loop for the stretchers to be held safely.

Hat pins are a collector's field of great passion with reference material in reasonable supply. The hats, though, that are available at fairs are more recent, usually from the 1920s to the 1950s. Look at the history of fashion and magazines of the period for styles and trade names of makers.

1. Openwork crochet gloves were made in natural, white or black. A little ribbon or bit of elastic tightened the wrist and sometimes ended in a bow. Well-laundered pairs will have slightly shrunken fingers. Never wash them in detergent, but use pure soap flakes and dry them on a glove-stretcher made of plastic.

An interesting sideline are the crochet patterns for different gloves which were sold right up to the 1950s; it would add to any collection. This pair in very good condition, £8.

2. A little papier-mâché glove box in typical Victorian scrollwork, painted with flowers and inlaid with mother of pearl in a birds and butterflies design.

Most would have been made in a set with a handkerchief box, although finding a matching pair with the exact design is not likely. In any case, the Victorians didn't really think that a set always had to match - only that the pattern should be similar.

Look at all the edges to make sure there are no bits knocked off - the scrolls are surprisingly fragile and damage is both frequent and expensive to repair well. So far, there are few really convincing fakes. C.1870s, £45.

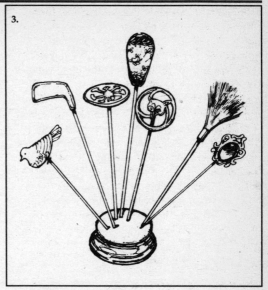

3. Hat pin collectors have inspired some good reference books. Check the Reference List if you plan to invest. Many pins are little gems, with silver or gold inlaid in precious stones. Others are bold fakes in plastic and glass, changing style with the fashions each year. Still others are delicate confections of feathers and ribbon.

Long hat pins, the most fun to collect, date from a very short period when long hair and big hats combined - about 1890-1920. Then hair became short, hats became small, and the pins followed suit. Indeed, long pins were outlawed in some American states as lethal weapons. Watch out for buttons or lapel pins pulled off and glued onto an old pin; you can usually see a clumsy join. £10-100.

4., 5. and **6.** Three hats from the 1950s, still jaunty in cotton and felt. Study magazines of the period and make a note of the many tradenames like Fredericks or Shilling. Look for their labels when you browse. This is still a fairly quiet area so you should find some good things. £10-18.

Gloves, Hats and Handbags

From long before Lady Bracknell spoke those resounding words, "in a *hand*bag?" no sensible lady would be without her capacious friend to hold the necessities of life. And in Victorian times, for intrepid travellers to the far corners of the earth, or just to the other side of the park, there would be two or three handkerchiefs, a money purse, a comb in a case, smelling salts in a vinaigrette, keys to her handbag and small dressing case, folding lorgnette, notebook, silver pen or pencil, jewel case, sewing kit and scissors, packets of migraine powders, pressed powder papers, a tiny glass bottle of cologne...no wonder bags were comfortably large, more like small suitcases. Many were so sturdy that they are barely scratched even today; often it's only the lock that will need replacing, or perhaps some corner pieces where the leather has rubbed.

COLLECTORS' NOTES

Look for rectangular shapes and square bases where the bag would rest on the floor or seat of a carriage or omnibus. Many have metal corners, especially at the base, or little brass studs to protect them. Nickel-plated frames were advertised for permanent stability.

Black and brown were the favoured colours as being suitable for all occasions. Morocco leather (goat skin tanned with sumac) was suggested; Russian leather was popular with a diamond-patterned surface. Canvas was left to the schoolboy or the games bag. Plush fabric and beadwork were suitable for evening wear.

Catalogues of the period, based on famous stores like the Army and Navy or respectable companies which specialised in what we would now call mail order, are a mine of information. The majority of women in the countryside chose from them for convenience and reliability.

There are no deliberate fakes, but many bags could be worn by royalty tomorrow, and few would know. Mild cracking of the leather and a well-worn interior, may be the best signs of age.

1.

1. I have never understood why these delightful beadwork bags do not bring higher prices. Worse for the dealer, better for the collector who has the sense to buy now. Victorian bags are rounded, often gathered slightly onto a metal frame. Designs are pretty and floral, in rich colours, often taking their theme from the mass-produced frame. Later, in the 1920s and 1930s, beaded bags were often flat and square or rectangular, very thin and with wonderful Art Deco scenic or geometric patterns in silver, green, blues and so on. The fabric handle was also beaded, or could be a thin chain. As prices are low, look for perfect examples with no missing beads or fraying edges. Beaded bags of the 1950s and 1960s made in France are thicker, heavier and should be stored for a few years. This Victorian bag, £30. 1920s bags, £6-36.

2. Put this in the latest fashion shot for *Vogue* and it could be your country tote bag for the winter. It was designed in 1875 and recommended for its discreet black cord decoration on long-wearing Morocco leather.

Precise dating is almost impossible and there are no labels to give you clues. Look at period catalogues for subtle differences in shapes and sizes; a modern version would be shorter or taller. £15.

3. A little extra the 1930s girl would have carried for an unexpected visit; only 2 cm long, £5.

4. Before we knew anything about endangered species, the dream of many a would-be sophisticated lady in the 1950s was a crocodile dressing case. This magnificent example in black, lined in beige watered silk, would have satisfied all her ambitions. There is a fitted mirror, dozens of little ruched silk bands to hold crystal bottles, and a general air of luxury and travel on the Orient Express. Because we are sensitive about wildlife today such cases bring relatively little money considering their original cost of more than £100. If fitted with all its bottles, £95. As it is, empty, just £30.

5. Fitted bags tell us about what people thought was a priority for travelling. This manicure kit of the 1950s doubled as a handbag with an ingenious hinged top. Bright red leather, almost unused, and complete with all pieces handled in red leather as well; £55.

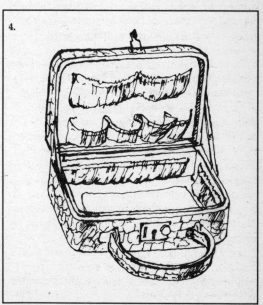

Inkstands and Accessories

The need to communicate by writing was and is responsible for some of the most delightful accessories ever invented. Early writing tools like styli and slates are rare and costly, but since the l8th century, inkwells and inkstands, with their accompanying pen and pencil holders, letter knives, stationery boxes and so on, seem to have touched the decorative instinct in designers and craftsmen the world over. The only problem for the collector is narrowing the potential by concentrating on a period or material; the choice is otherwise embarrassingly large. A problem which may not be shared by computer or word processor collectors in 3001.

COLLECTORS' NOTES

Inkstands have attracted reproduction merchants for some time, but most so far are in brass or fake ormolu, with an over-bright gold finish and no trace of ink in the wells.

Ceramic or glass wells should also show some dirt or residue inside, and perhaps in crevices around the top where ink spilled as the well was filled. However, I do have two or three myself which are undoubtedly Victorian or earlier and which show no sign of ink at all. Like little vases, the more decorative pieces may have stayed on the desk or side table for looks rather than use.

Extensive desk sets of many matching pieces are a fairly new invention. Turn-of-the-century correspondents kept a single compact stationery box which included a place for paper, slides for pens and wells for ink bottles. Such boxes and slopes were opened up when needed and folded up when the writer was finished. (See also Boxes, and Pens and Pencils.)

Inkstands of an affordable nature mostly date from the mid-19th century. Many come apart for cleaning and repair because inkwells of glass and china were replaced regularly. Make sure all the parts are there - little holes or clips with no apparent purpose usually mean a missing pen holder or decorative finial.

1. This matching set is rare for the period - most desks displayed a variety of pieces, both in material and in design. Inkwell, candlestick, letter opener and pen tray are in silver plate, 1830s, £95-100. It would be nearer £350 for hallmarked silver. Extras may have included a letter rack, a stamp box and perhaps a cigar lighter. Egyptian motifs were very popular after Napoleon's expedition in the 1790s.

2.

3. A porcelain inkwell with flowers and butterflies and a rope edge. There may have been a matching porcelain-handled pen. Check edges for chips. No mark but very collectable. 1890s, £45, English.

4. Folding leather stationery case; watch out for missing fittings and poor condition. "Leather" cloth cannot be restored. They were carried in suitcases for travel and are often badly rubbed. £20 up, or as little as £5.

2. A letter opener of mother of pearl, with a delicate gilt Art Nouveau clasp. Look out for sharp edges where the metal mount might have twisted or broken. Fripperies like this are very collectable, but they should be in immaculate condition. Broken mounts ruin the investment value.

Be very careful cleaning mother of pearl. Many cleaning fluids destroy the pearl surface forever. 1890-1905, £20-25.

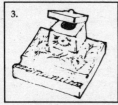

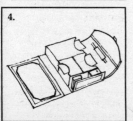

6. Victorian papier-mâché painted with flowers and ribbons. Glass inkwells and a stamp box mean the fittings are complete.

Papier-mâché is quite strong, but edges are liable to damage. Check that the fittings are original; they should fit snugly into their spaces. £55-65. With mother of pearl inlay and a more unusual design, the price could be £150.

7. Copper Art Nouveau inkstand, holding a single well with glass inset. The design is stamped out so that the inner metal shows a reverse design. Look for good patina as this period is now very popular and often faked. £25.

8. Found as a lump of black rust, it took three weeks of cleaning to uncover this c.1910 stand of painted metal with china wells; originally gold and green, with an impressed violet design. Austrian maker. Bought for £2, worth about £25.

5. A brass travelling ink-well, the inner cover held down by a clip and a padded outer lid making sure not a drop escapes. These are highly collect-able and come in many different metals and sizes. 1850-1910, this, c.1870, £30. Smaller ones from £15.

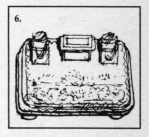

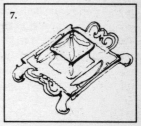

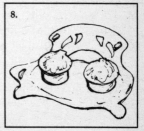

Jewellery

The value of jewellery is threefold; first in its materials, then in its craft, and finally in fashion and design. Whereas costume jewellery depends almost entirely on the last, jewellery made with precious and semi-precious materials is pretty evenly divided. At our budget level and its small pieces, the pendulum swings again to craft and fashion; there is not enough actual material to make much of a difference.

The Industrial Revolution created a new industry of mass-produced jewellery. From the late 19th century to today, only some middle-range pieces would be hand finished, and an even smaller number were hand-made.

COLLECTORS' NOTES

Silver was used for early antique diamond settings and for much enamelled jewellery as well. The Renaissance use of enamel detail, as complex as a mediaeval illumination, gradually disappeared by the end of the 18th century, to be revived wholeheartedly by the Victorian passion for the mediaeval and the Gothic.

During the 20th century enamelling was used again to give colour and pattern without bulk. Both Art Nouveau and Art Deco designs relied heavily on enamelled surfaces, mostly on silver.

However, chipped enamel loses so much of its value that it is often repainted to disguise the damage. Hold an enamelled piece near your eye and up to the light and tilt it back and forth, looking for breaks in the surface or minute changes in colour which will show up a repair.

Danish silver jewellery of the 1930s-1960s is bold and chunky; bracelets of smooth links are marked "silver" and "Denmark". Even the early designs can look very modern, so find the maker's mark if possible and do some research.

American silver jewellery is always marked sterling, even clasps - if not, it is silver plated.

English silver jewellery is usually hallmarked, but small pieces like fine earrings, clasps, tiny beads, etc., need not be by law.

1. and **2.** Delicate engraved silver earrings from the Victorian period are still available in considerable quantity and can make a fascinating collection on their own.

The designs are almost infinite; many are decorated with niello, in which the lines of an engraved design are filled with a black alloy made of lead, copper, silver and sulphur. When the piece was heated the alloy set hard, and could later be polished smooth. It is very effective, but it does get worn with continual polishing.

Earrings were also decorated with thin silver wire, either smooth or in the form of beading. More expensive designs included gold inlay and Etruscan designs with heavy geometric borders; all would probably have had a brooch to match. c.1860-1900; depending on size and weight, £18-40. Only brooches and lockets were generally marked.

3. The Art Deco period was a fruitful one; chrome was the favoured metal in furniture, silver in jewellery. Although the finest pieces might be made in platinum, known since the Victorian period, silver was used for a great deal of the smaller pieces like this wonderful design in green and black enamel on silver, set with very tiny diamond chips.

Cheating on price, maybe - I bought the earrings one week, then decided I had to have the pin as well and went back the second week. C.1925, earrings £75, brooch £50.

4. Typical of the light jewellery probably bought originally for a young girl.

The silver chain is prettily worked in open links, the pink rose quartz beads and the pendant stone are cut well, and the whole is both delicate and youthful. Very inexpensive for such a pretty piece, c,1920, £12.

5. Cameos are carved from shells or from layered hardstones. Both use the different coloured layers to convey depth and shadow, and range from fairly simple classical portraits to quite complex scenes. Hardstone cameos are the most valuable and can date from Roman times on. Shell cameos were popular from the 19th century, made in Italy and exported round the world.

Watch out for 20th century cheap imitations in pressed glass; they won't bear a second look, but at a distance they can be quite convincing. This 1910s shell cameo set, £90, is set in marcasite borders - iron pyrites cut and mounted close together, usually in silver, to increase their natural sparkle.

Jewellery

Ancient gold jewellery can be studied in many museums, and it's always a wonder how such very fragile artifacts have triumphantly survived their burial. But survive they do, with values much increased by their history.

The modest gold jewellery within our budget is mainly from the late 19th century onwards, often bought for its wearability and interest rather than pure assayed value, and ultimately for giving something special to our children. I'd suggest making a quick record of anything you know; it may seem ridiculous, but in another hundred years, a great-granddaughter will be pleased to find out more about her inheritance.

COLLECTORS' NOTES

Gold can be hallmarked, but most small jewellery has no space for the complete set, and by custom it is marked simply with the carat, 1 unit out of 24; 9K - 9 parts gold to 15 parts other metals - (usually silver), 15K - 15 parts gold to 9 parts other metal, or 22K - 22 parts gold to 2 parts silver. American jewellery seldom uses 9K, but make much use of 14K, 18K and 24K.

9K gold has been used a great deal for inexpensive rings and earrings. It is judged much inferior to 15K, and other things being equal, always choose the higher carats.

Rolled gold is the equivalent of cheap gold plate, and its value is minimal. However, long chains for a gold locket or pendant were often made of rolled gold over sterling silver. The label may be marked correctly, but sometimes the actual piece has no markings at all.

If you are going to invest in jewellery you should buy a proper glass loupe and learn how to identify the various precious and semi-precious stones.

Pearls have been made artificially since Roman times; the standard now is cultured pearls grown around a mother of pearl bead. Cheap plastic and fish paste can be easily identified; the hole for stringing will be rough and flaky.

1. This little hand is wide enough to clip a string of pearls together, its original purpose. The Victorians loved hands of all kinds, but this is a 1920s copy; 15K, and £23-28.

2. From the 1930s, an extending gold cigarette holder with an ivory tip. Very swish, and with no filter as modern holders might have, the long flank is engine turned in different patterns. Hallmarked for 22K and maker's mark for 1937, £55. Collectors of smoking paraphernalia would also appreciate this.

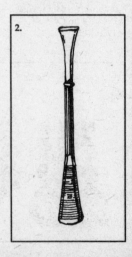

3.

4.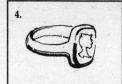

5.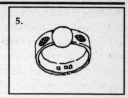

3. Rings are the easiest purchase when you are looking for gold jewellery at an affordable level. There are so many around that every antique fair must have at least two dozen cabinets. This Victorian turquoise and seed pearl ring of 15K is pretty and desirable. £65.

4. A cornelian intaglio, incised rather than carved as a cameo is. Sometimes used as seals, the carving is a portrait head, the ring itself 22K. Cornelians are a dull-red chalcedony, one of the quartz stones which include agates and onyx. The high gold content and the stone make it £75.

5. A mourning ring, the shaft enclosing a braid of hair. The centre monogram is blank; it may have been a friendship ring, kept in commercial stock. Hair jewellery is not popular with our more queasy sensibilities, so a fairly low price of £35 matches the 9K gold.

6. A Victorian bar brooch. Some had ornamental motifs, but many used stones whose initials spelled out a name, or a word like dear or sweet. This one, only 9K, but with a tiny diamond, emerald, aquamarine and ruby. £80. Good stones, poor gold.

7. Anyone who has read Agatha Christie will remember Miss Marple's bog oak brooch, made from peat-preserved black oak, and used for much sober jewellery. This pair of elegant earrings with bog oak graduated beads set in 9K gold, c.1880, £55.

8. Lockets were another Victorian pleasure. A young lady could keep a picture of her mother, her betrothed or a memento inside. This symbolic lock and key clasp, holding finely engraved gold links, has a tiny glass-fronted space inside the garnet-set lock. It is beautifully made and in 15K would easily bring double its 9K value of £100.

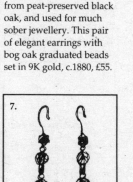

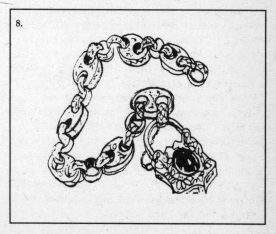

Kitchenware

With the renewed interest in the history of domestic life, tools and equipment - once thrown away when new replacements were available - are now cherished. To see, perhaps, toasters and coffee grinders we bought for our own kitchens now finding pride of place in a 1950s or 1960s arts display is a lesson in changing values!

Collecting antique and more recent kitchenware is a working asset for the cook. With reasonable care, much of it can be used. And on the whole it's still a reasonable price. The craftsmanship and variety is truly amazing; everyone can find things which are unique, because they've been made or adapted for local use, adding a special delight to the hunt.

COLLECTORS' NOTES

Condition, as always, is important, but with kitchenware it takes on a slightly different aspect. By its very nature kitchenware has been in active use, and often hard use at that. Of course, the perfectly preserved kitchen antique, something bought but never used, does exist, but that is really very rare. In some cases, in fact, it acts almost as a deterrent since kitchen collectors like to think of those generations of family life, baking, boiling and serving up twenty-course meals both upstairs and downstairs.

The collector must assess the difference between natural wear and tear, and subsequent damage. Well-repaired damage, during the object's active life, and particularly if contemporary more or less with the piece, can be an asset for social historians, although it may sometimes affect the price adversely.

So far restoration in its grand sense rather than useful repair has not really taken hold in the affordable market nor, until recently, has fakery, but both are on the increase. Over-restoration is usually the work of interior designers, looking for "focal points" in their rooms. Old kitchenware can be cleaned and polished, but should never, ever, be repainted for display.

1. A late Georgian cutlery box, in dark glowing oak, with centuries of polishing to give it that unmistakable patina. The simplest versions are straight-edged, sometimes with a scrolled handle as the only decoration. £65.

2. The essential ingredient of all country kitchens - the big iron pot. A magnificent cauldron, still good for another 150 years of soup; the mould lines show this is 19th century, cast in two halves over a clay core. Those with rounded bottoms and no feet hung from a chimney crane. Watch out for too-clean interiors in new ones. £55.

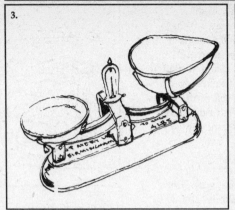

3. Scales are a perennial favourite, although they do take up a lot of room when you buy more than three or four pieces!

The most attractive have some individual detail, like the central pointer of the balance in this 1850s example. All the fittings are in brass, with the base in cast iron.

Both bowls are original, as are the set of weights, each marked with a number. Missing bowls get replaced all too often, so make sure yours fit properly in their cradle. Watch out for ones that are buckled or twisted.

If a single weight is missing, you may have to buy a complete set as they can be amazingly individual once you have seen a group together.

Don't be tempted to re-paint or re-gild the name on the base; collectors get very upset and it will affect the resale price. £95, and very much up.

4. A large sieve like this was not used in the kitchen, but collectors now hang them against the wall to admire their varied woven centres. They were used for different grains, according to the size of the openings; smaller ones with fine mesh were for flour at home. Make sure the mesh isn't broken. From £5-45, depending on the size and pattern. Look for local weaves.

5. The value of trivets lie in their many patterns and decorative appearance. But they also vary with use; long-handled ones kept your hands safe from the heat, half-circles stood against the grate, barred ones hung on the fender. These have been widely faked; look for unusual designs, but beware of similar patterns turning up everywhere, very clean underneath. £12-20.

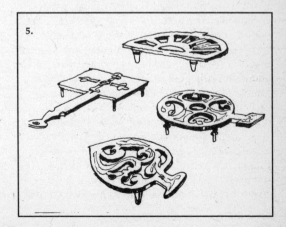

Kitchenware

Restoration of period homes rather than replacement or modernisation has meant that thousands of genuine Victorian kitchens have been rescued from oblivion. Television and books show how these kitchens looked and what kind of equipment they used. While restorers try to recreate the appearance of the last century, few would dare tell the cook to use Victorian tools - but they are sought after just the same for decoration and interest.

What was once the province of a few researchers has become a very busy market; we've invented a name, kitchenalia, with shops and stalls devoted to cooking and household tools of the past. Unhappily, new admirers have been followed by the copies, so the serious collector needs to keep a very sharp eye out for spurious objects.

COLLECTORS' NOTES

Elaborate decoration is rare in Anglo-Saxon kitchenware, so be wary of non-essential ornament, especially the kind which is easily added. Carving on a wooden spoon, if it looks appropriate and attractive, may well be genuine, while painting or stencilling is more suspect. On the other hand, an addition made years ago for a genuine purpose (lettering or labels on small chests of drawers or shelves) can add greatly to charm and unfortunately also to price.

We've noted before that outright fakes are common in metalwork, and kitchenware is full of metal. Some of it looks very good, with increased attention being paid to careful reproduction. Many of these pleasant pieces have been made by hand in the traditional way; evidence of mass manufacturing, which used to be an good sign of fakery, is no longer infallible.

The patina of age, though, is harder to imitate. Brass tends to acquire a dark glow which is unmistakable; unfortunately copper is often scoured clean in normal use, taking away useful clues along with the dirt.

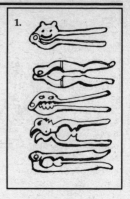

1. Nutcrackers have been reasonably common in Europe for a long time; there's a note in court records that Henry VIII gave a pair to Anne Boleyn. Early examples are wood, often carved in fantastic animal heads. Brass and silver pairs were sold neatly boxed with a set of nut picks to accompany them.

Cast brass lends itself to such novelties as, among the models above, a squirrel holding the nuts in its tummy, a rather obvious but daring design for a pair of legs cracking the nut between them, and a noble eagle's head, with scrolled handles. That one is possibly American, or made for the American market, as during the late 19th century the eagle was a particularly popular symbol of that newly growing country. A collection of nutcrackers should include at least one carved wood example. £12- 28.

2. A late Victorian cutlery tray in basketwork with a practical baize lining. Nothing to polish, easy to keep clean, c.1875, £25-30.

Watch out for torn corners on the cloth, and especially for broken stems on the rim and edges of the basketwork. They can be quite sharp and scratch the table as well as hands. Worse, they are hard to repair except by a professional.

3. Rolling pins in china are rare; with flower painting rarer still. So this pretty and practical pin with a pierced end for hanging will cost something over £45. Plainer ones from £18.

4. Jelly appeared on Victorian menus with regularity. It was inexpensive and simple to make, good for you, child-like in its appeal and pretty to look at. To make it even prettier, the best jelly moulds were made with a china decorated core, which stayed in place when the outer mould was taken away. This left the pattern showing through the jewel colours.

Quite hard to find both pieces intact, so this is £90-£95 or even up to £250.

5. Victorians preferred their aspic, fish, beef, vegetables, rice and pudding dishes in moulds, and the kitchenware manufacturers responded. They were made in earthenware, copper, pewter, tin and glass. Look for the more complicated designs like pineapples, bowls of fruit, ears of corn; these simpler ones, £15-30; more unusual designs £40-90.

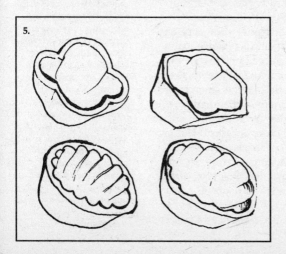

Kitchenware

Edwardian cooks could look around and think they had come a long way. Perhaps the greatest achievement was the use of gas for lighting and cooking. The first gas cooker we know of was actually made in 1878, but it wasn't commonly available before the turn of the century. But even the new coal ranges had controllable ovens and water tanks for the first supply of hot water.

There were other helping hands, too; a mincing machine, a cake mixer with two revolving blades, a bread slicer (one of the best was imported from Norway) and a hundred other little chore-cutters - the day of the gadget had arrived.

Within twenty years, fitted kitchens of a sort were being offered - albeit with only one or two matching cabinets. Servants went off to war and didn't come back into the home, and books were published for the dashing young lady or bachelor who had to manage a very small household on an even smaller income. The world - and the kitchen - had changed forever.

COLLECTORS' NOTES
Looking for kitchenalia and household tools of this period can be very disconcerting as the shape and the purpose seem contemporary; only the material will suggest its proper age.

Carpet sweepers date from 1840, vacuum cleaners from 1904 and the Hoover first appeared in 1908 in America. A mad and wonderful Baby Daisy model in England needed two people to operate it - that didn't last long, but examples can still be found. One place that reproduction hasn't reached is these larger souvenirs of our past.

Look for any equipment with labels or instructions, even if badly torn or faded. It is sometimes the only way to trace an object's history. For smaller collections, concentrate on something easy to display but with lots of variety - ladles, ice cream scoops, tea strainers, a particular kind of pottery. I have acquired twenty totally different lemon squeezers just a year after finding my first one.

1. Everyone knows about Mrs Beeton, but few know Mrs Randall, Countess Morphy, and hundreds of other writers from the late 19th century onwards. Specialist booksellers in cookery usually have a catalogue and mailing list, but many finds have been in with general stock.

The range is so vast that you should limit yourself, perhaps to a subject like baking or fish, or a period. The richest mine right now is between 1890 and 1940. Most books from that period are still affordable - only a very few titles reach £50, yet the contents are often full of amusing and genuine information, with detailed descriptions of utensils, suggestions for unusual recipes and advice on every possible subject.

Look for stylised illustrations, especially drawings by well-known artists of the period. Watch out for damaged bindings, missing pages or bad stains. A dust jacket is a great asset to the collector - don't throw your new ones away! This 1914 title on meal planning, £15. Similar titles, £5-30.

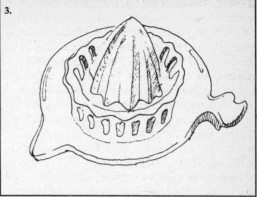

2. Terrine for pâté. Watch out for tops that don't quite fit the base. This small, well-painted duck, probably Continental, c.1920, £58.

Kitchen china is often unmarked, like this one. Quality decoration can make up for missing attribution if the piece is sufficiently attractive. But then it *must* be in perfect condition. Watch out for minute cracks under the knob or head.

3. Last year I bought this white porcelain lemon squeezer with its registration mark for 1907, otherwise unmarked. The drainer is linked on top with a series of scallops, and the handle fits over the finger. It combines form and function to perfection. I know of no other like it.

I now have a stoneware 1920s' reamer and cup, a Bandalasta plastic blue and white one, a tiny Japanese model in basketweave porcelain, a 1930s' pottery one, like a boat, with the reamer as a sail...At this price level, you can afford to buy only tip-top condition, no chips or cracks. My original find would be £25, but it's not for sale!

4. A spoon rack in classic French provincial style, probably 1940s, painted in rubbed blue. The border is carved in triangles. Pretty and useful, therefore eminently saleable. £20-28.

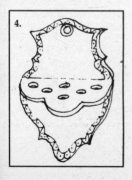

5. Waiting for a world that will never happen again, a perfect Edwardian maid. This little porcelain egg-timer must have amused the bachelor cook at breakfast every morning. Continental, unmarked as so many of these trinkets are, and mass-produced. About six or seven different figures were made, one a dancer, another a Scots piper, etc. All had a space for the timer on a cork to be slipped into a hand, the choice of figure in accordance to the wishes of the customer. £12-15.

Lamps and Candlesticks

Nothing has changed our lives more than artificial light. Without the use of some sort of aid to night vision we would be condemned to an existence regulated solely by the sun and the moon. If fire brought us heat and sustained us through the cold time of the year, surely the discovery, first of candles and then gas and electricity in particular with its endless potential to suit every need, is close to the miracle of social development.

COLLECTORS' NOTES

Candlesticks are very versatile, taking up only a little space and providing an attractive display on a dining table even when not in use.

Pairs of silver candlesticks, even Victorian and Edwardian copies, are way above our price. Single sticks bring only a quarter of the price, but they are still expensive, and most modest collectors will have to be content with silver plate, or Sheffield plate, which was made in considerable quantity in the 19th century.

Many are not of good quality, being thinly cast and weighted with pitch or plaster hidden under green baize.

Watch out for extremely thin areas in all sticks where the silver has been polished away to almost nothing. Because of the light metal, sticks can sometimes bend to one side; it can be very difficult to straighten them out.

Candlesticks were also made in a wide variety of materials, far less expensive than silver. The open twist in wood is a favourite, and when mounted top and bottom with silver or brass, they are very handsome indeed. But watch out for cracks in the wood. They can be repaired, but you may lose the patina of the original finish.

Small chambersticks were carried up to bed. They are short with a little dish underneath and they were made not only in silver but in brass, pewter, tin, Britannia metal and ceramics, even in glass. Some have an attached snuffer, but these are rare and that makes them costly.

1. The traditional silver stick, made from the 18th century onwards.

Stroke the fluting with your fingers. If you can feel sharp edges, the quality is generally good. Cast columns are blunter and all the detail looks a little blurred. Silver plate, c.1920s, £45-65.

2. Twisted oak in brass. Look for clean joins and good patina. Watch out for damage where the metal has been pushed down; some are screwed in. C.1915, marked Maple Ltd., £22.

3. Another traditional shape; a Victorian table lustre, with its long drops and painted glass centre. Take care; the candle burning down can crack the glass. A pair would be a find; this single, c.1880, £55. Check that all the drops are the same; there should be seven to ten.

4. Every Victorian parlour had a piano and every piano had two swinging arms (top illustration) to light the music stand. During the change from Victorian taste to Art Deco, most of the pianos and their sconces were thrown away. Now a beautifully scrolled pair in the market sells at once, though pianos are a little slower in returning to fashion. Make sure the arms swing easily. C.1890, £50.

The double wall sconce below is later, with its Art Nouveau curves. These are easy to adapt for electric wiring. Be careful of too-good condition; they are from a reproduction house. Genuine 1900s, £45-55. In pewter, £95.

5., 6. and **7.** The Victorian passion for the exotic knew no bounds. These are only a few of the strange shapes and even stranger images that were used to make ornamental candlesticks and other goods. **5.** Two of the macabre use of dead animal limbs - mounted with great skill in silver and horn, but we find them so unpleasant that they are really quite inexpensive; c.1880, £12 and £20. **6.** The mysterious East, in Indian brass with a ruby-red candle-holder; c.1890, £30. **7.** The mysterious West; an Indian totem pole out of an early Western; c.1875, £65.

Lamps and Candlesticks

For the collector, this is a subject which offers utility as well as aesthetic satisfaction. On the whole we buy lamps to use rather than simply stand on a shelf, so one of the prime pre-requisites will be whether they can be used safely. The wonders of electricity notwithstanding, old wiring can be lethal; have it looked at by a professional.

COLLECTORS' NOTES

With any kind of lamp or chandelier, we are in the realm of interior design. Lighting to be used means looking carefully at where they will be placed. Many antique lamps are either too short or too tall as reading lights, and chandeliers need to accommodate a reasonable wattage to look their best without being overcome by too-brilliant or too-glaring bulbs.

If you buy sconces or piano sticks without their shades, or you want to adapt them to electricity, be careful about the added weight. Many brass arms were not meant to bear a heavy shade, even if they look quite strong. You will find they pull out of the wall, or turn upside down. Try to choose lamps that still have their own shades. They should match not only in general period, but in shape and form.

Chandeliers are not only made as waterfalls of fine crystal drops; there are smaller antique ceiling lights from hallways and bedrooms which are perfect for modern homes. Be careful that the glass shade fits properly; high up on the ceiling any failure or fall can be especially dangerous.

If the chandelier or ceiling fitting has many small parts, check them all. Even when you find something that looks perfect, ask to have it taken down so you can look carefully at each part, especially those in cast iron or brass. What looks fantastic ten feet up may be full of fissures and broken bits when you see it at eye level. That's one advantage of fair stalls; they are only up temporarily, so the lamps usually hang where you can see them from all sides and the top.

1.

1. These small desk lights replaced the large oil lamps which burned in every room until the turn of the century.

Thin-legged Edwardian furniture wouldn't have been able to take the heavy iron fittings anyway, so these light bits of brass were the perfect pairing to the similarly light chairs and tables. The cream glass shade is quite thin, and the lamp would look at home today in almost any room, on a desk or dressing table. C.1915, £35-40.

2. Centre lights on a hanging gimbal are often called barn lights, for no reason that I can discover. Certainly no barn I have ever seen would need anything like this. No point in wondering, but this particular one, one of a set of four c.1895, was originally made for gas; the tube goes through the hollow circle. They still have their taps as well as the deflector which dissipates the heat from the gas flame. Original, perfect, as a single, £95.

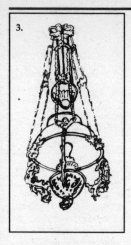

5. In the 1920s and 1930s, lighting was heavily influenced by Hollywood and its stage sets. Marbled glass was back in favour, especially in cream, greens and beiges, all 1930s colouring.

Everyone wanted diffused light thrown up onto the ceiling instead of down onto the furniture. Thousands of new-style "bag" lights were made, the one, two or three-bulb light fitting hidden by its container of glass. Early examples had rich stained-glass colouring to imitate the Tiffany studio, but in the 1930s that style was discarded, and trend-setting lights with pale marbling and shiny chrome rims were put up instead. These are not quite back in favour, hence the low cost. Check that the glass has no cracks or chips, and the chrome is not peeling. £25-45.

3. A marriage; what should be a Victorian rise and fall is in fact made up. The lead weight and its chains are probably original; two of the arms are one pattern, the third is different and the shade is modern. Yet ten feet up it looks fine! £50 if you spot the fake, £300 if it were genuinely period.

4. Another gas light; the condition is perfect, with the design acid-etched on the shade matching the scrollwork on the lamp. Wiring through tubes looks good but it can lead to trouble if there is wear which cannot be seen. C.1900, one of a four; as a single, £95, but £600 for the complete set for a hall.

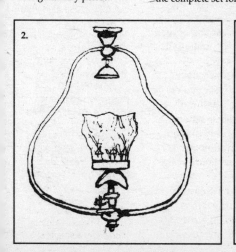

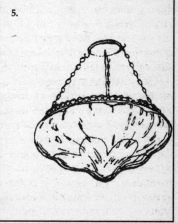

Linen and Laundry

A cupboard or chest full of the best linen her family could afford was the first prerequisite of any bride. Her dowry included all the sheets, pillow cases, quilts, coverlets and table linen she had made and embroidered, or at the very least, monogrammed, while waiting to use them in her own first household. But from the first part of this century, buying linen at a specialist shop replaced most of the home embroidery.

The Americans called the young lady's cupboard a Dower or Hope Chest. Any woman today must resent the suggestion that her only Hope was marriage, but to be honest, we are now enjoying the result; every fair has its linen stall - everything freshly washed and starched, frills neatly ironed, smelling of lavender or pot pourri.

COLLECTORS' NOTES

At the affordable level, there are few old pieces available. Most of the linen on display comes from the end of the 19th century right up to the 1940s, and it falls into two main categories: professional plain and embroidered work, and amateur projects, no matter how skilled, made for someone's own home.

The first generally includes underclothes, night-dresses, children's christening dresses, and the best tablecloths and place mats. There is a vague assumption that our grandmothers sat and sewed all day, but for most families that was no longer the case; orders were taken by the new department stores or household shops. Buyers can see from the quantity around that white-on-white embroidery and lace was the favoured combination, easy to fit into any colour scheme.

Home workers were occasionally very skilled, but projects for their own use usually meant less complicated designs and colour combinations to suit their clothes or their rooms.

Look for linen without damage to the cloth; holes or frayed threads in lace or embroidery are easier to repair without being too visible.

1. and **2.** Linen means laundry and that means irons. Solid irons, heated in front of the fire, had to be thoroughly cleaned before touching the cloth. Some were heated with an iron slug, which kept the iron itself a little cleaner; these box irons are still around for about £25-30. Others, like the French iron (**1.**) and the simpler English one (**2.**) were heated by charcoal. An ornamental clip closed and opened the base. Brass knobs controlled the air flow and holes below let out fumes. Both late 19th century, **1.** £70, **2.** £55. More unusual handles or models make up to £600! Box irons have been copied lately; look for signs of real use.

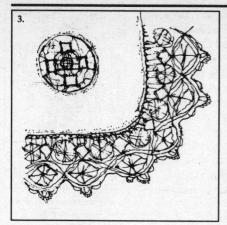

3.

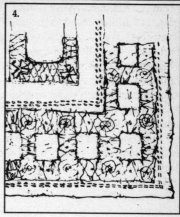

4.

3. Crochet was used mainly from the 1850s on as a substitute for bobbin lace. The simple tambour hook and some thread was all that was required. The skilled use of crochet swept Ireland first; some of the finest with raised flowers and padded motifs is known as Irish Crochet. Patterns were taken from lace models, and pattern books in many villages made reading and writing unnecessary for local workers; they could copy what they needed directly from the book.

By 1910, when this centre cloth was made, the cost of similar bobbin lace insertions alone would have been more than the price of the finished cloth.

Look for the few stitches and many different patterns. You can still buy small bits and pieces to make up your own pattern book. This cloth, £22.

4. The loveliest white embroidery is Ayrshire work, from its production in that Scottish county c.1850-1900. It's a form of cut-work made of white cotton on white muslin, and even the most richly embroidered christening robes and cloths sell for under £200. This pillow case is only £20; a similar sheet might reach £60. Don't attempt repairs unless you are experienced in needlework.

5. The influence of Anne Macbeth continued throughout the 20th century (see p. 72-73). Home needlewomen in the 1920s adapted her ideas for appliqué to all their household needs.

This tablecloth is in tones of green on a natural ground, over-cast with black edging. The work is very skilled and it was probably made for sale at a speciality shop catering for the home. £45.

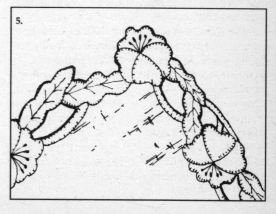

5.

Locks and Keys

From time immemorial, we have wanted to keep things to ourselves. At first, perhaps, it was only some food or precious tools wrapped up under a bed. Later, it might have been bits of jewellery or a special pot, a religious or sacred object or even a particular room or temple which needed to be kept safe from the prying eyes of outsiders. In small tribal groups the force of social sanctions had been enough protection, but once villages grew into towns and cities, such accepted taboos disappeared and the concept of the bar and the lock was born. By biblical times, references to locked doors and bolts, and locked treasure boxes are common.

Doors were fitted with the simplest form of lock, a beam or bar across the opening, held by staples and shifted back and forth by hand. Most societies developed some sort of variation to allow access from both sides, but only to authorised people. And so the lock and key were created.

The principles of making a lock have not changed much in the last four millennia. The earliest known lock dates from Sargon's palace at Khorsabad, Assyria, and references have allowed archaeologists to date the first locks to the ancient Egyptians. Although examples of these first locks are obviously not available except in museum collections, the same principles were used right up to and including the Yale lock and key of the 19th century.

Only in the past century has the lock become so necessary that it is used everywhere. Along with such proliferation, security has become the *raison d'être*, and decorative qualities have been entirely ignored.

Happily for the enthusiast, locks (and keys in particular) of many more artistic locksmithery traditions do exist. Today we are left with a wonderful history to collect as a reminder of a time when function and form could be integrated to make even the most prohibitive lock and key an object of beauty.

1. The oldest known form of lock invented by the ancient Egyptians was little recognised in the West until Napoleon's expedition to Egypt in 1798. Danon's engraving, above, was made during that time. A collection which included such illustrations would be truly fascinating. £55, from a second edition of 1825.

The construction is shown clearly. A block of wood held pins which fell to different lengths, but which could be pushed up to leave a level surface. The block was fixed just above the sliding bar, drilled to allow the pins to fall and keep the bar from moving; the door was effectively locked.

The bar was hollowed out and a long, crooked wooden key was made, with fixed pins of corresponding lengths set in one end. The key was manipulated until its prongs pushed the pins up and the bolt was withdrawn. With a hole made in the door, the door could be opened from the inside or the outside.

2. A great disadvantage of the Egyptian key was its considerable size and weight. It had to be carried like a sickle across the shoulder. By the height of the Roman Empire, locksmiths were making smaller locks and much smaller iron keys, found in excavations all over the Italian peninsula. Their locks - which are much scarcer than keys and generally not available to the public - were like our modern padlocks. They could be carried easily on pack horse bags and shipping crates, both of which were constantly in use around the Empire. They even thought of making the key shaft hollow so that any dirt could be pushed right the way through - sometimes claimed as a modern improvement. This type of key, of which there are many variations, around £95. After the Roman period, there is a gap; the Celts of south-west England supposedly had wooden locks similar to Egyptian ones, brought by the Phoenicians. By the Middle Ages, there are records in Kent and Winchester of a thriving locksmith industry.

3. The decoration of lock plates and escutcheons reached its highest form on the Continent with German and French locksmiths in particular; their work is now very expensive. The English were more restrained and some of their work of the 16th and 17th centuries is still affordable, just; this key with its decorative handle is c.1690 and £90.

4. History in retrospect. Any house being mediaevalised to suit their Arts and Crafts owners had to have corresponding locks on the front door. This bronzed brass version of a Pugin design dates from c.1875 and would be £85-95.

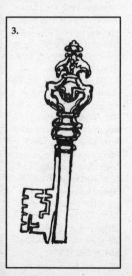

Locks and Keys

With the end of the 18th century, a new period of extreme practicality began to dominate locksmithery, especially in Britain where decorative work had never reached the heights of the Continental craft. Security was the order of the day - the Victorians had every reason to look for possessive reassurance in their increasingly volatile world, and the modern locksmith came to the fore. Here Britain had no equal - Barron, Bramah and Chubb, and the only American, Yale, are names which have become familiar to almost everyone in the population.

COLLECTORS' NOTES

Collectors of locks and keys seem to fall into the same categories as those of clocks and watches; some are fascinated by the function and the mechanical workings, and an early Barron's lock with two double-acting tumblers will be a source of delight, and some who are happy with the key or lockplate more or less on its own, either as a decorative shape or an historic or even a current symbol (i.e. the presentation of the keys of a town or university).

Happily they come together in the first instance as a matter of finance; for all the older examples, keys will be most affordable, most accessible, and most decorative to collect. Once, however, into modern times, it is quite possible to build a collection of either kind, depending on your own interests and ability to track down reference material and the relatively few experts in locks whose knowledge is available to outsiders. Most have been employed by the well-known lock companies mentioned above and any research could well start with them, as there are few general reference books to help you on the way.

There is one precious asset to the collector; few casual market or antique fair browsers appreciate the extraordinary history of that basic mechanical object on our front door or wardrobe, and this should make it possible to assemble quite a remarkable collection in a very short time.

1. The letter lock is nothing new - there is a reference in Beaumont and Fletcher's *The Noble Gentleman* which dates from 1615, a line reads "with a strange lock that opens with AMEN".

A letter lock works by using a word or sequence of letters. Removing the endpiece gives access to the inner ring, the letters are set and then the outer rings spun around to avoid leaving any clues. Four is the usual number, and the principle has been adapted to electronic use in many alarms and locks of all kinds today.

Aside from the padlock shown above made by Chubb, c.1924 and about £12, there are other keyless locks: with dials, with time settings and some ingenious inventions including a water-operated lock which only opens when so many drops of water tip over a lever. Many can be very large, but diagrams and illustrations can take the place of objects.

2. There have been some very strange lock designs as the world searched for a guarantee of total security.

Friend's Secret Lock c.1825, had a combination and a portable metal plate; both had to be inserted before the lock would open. Mr Machin's lock of the next year had a key with an expanding end which was drawn out of its shaft as various levers were turned, said to be total protection against lock-picking. And Gottlieb's Lock relied on a continual supply of paper being threaded across the keyhole to show instantly if anyone had tried to open it. Linus Yale might have stayed just as impractical, but his father was a locksmith already, and the young Yale Junior, c.1848 put his artistic talents to work, developing the rotating cylinder lock now used by the world for basic door protection. A series of Yale locks from the early period would be fascinating and this triple hole key alone from their first models is £45. Later keys had a solid handle.

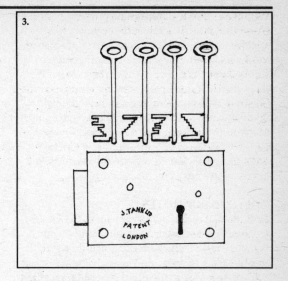

3.

3. and 4. Modern locks are not all deprived of attractive appearance. Above, this change key lock of c.1926 creates a strong abstract design. The earliest change key locks were patented in 1833; all keys could be used at various times, but any one of the keys used for locking would have to be used for that particular unlocking. This gave security when two or more people had access to one lock. £15 complete.

The lockless keys in the illustration below show that when given a chance modern locksmiths had as good a time as any Renaissance craftsmen, with openwork tops and eccentric wards. 19th and early 20th century brass, £4-8.

2.

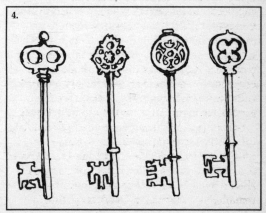

4.

Metalware

Metalware is so well represented in the antiques world that it seems almost perverse to have such a wide-ranging title where we cannot do justice to its variety. But the usual decorative metals - silver, copper and brass - have their own sections, and here, briefly, are notes and illustrations on some of the remaining metals of interest to collectors. Metalware needs to be identified in order to judge its period, authenticity, and of course, condition. With the great technical changes in the 19th century, that is not always easy nor straightforward.

COLLECTORS' NOTES

Antique metals fall into two main categories: ferrous, or iron-based, and non ferrous. Ferrous metals, which all rust, include wrought iron, cast iron, and steel.

Tinplate is steel with a thin coat of tin on either side; this keeps it clean, but once the layer of tin is breached it rusts quite badly, so we have included it with the irons.

Iron can be worked in three important ways. Forging is used for wrought iron; the heat and the hammering consolidate the iron and make it strong. It is also more malleable when hot and can be used as creatively as any lighter metal.

Casting in moulded forms is quicker and cheaper, especially useful for models taken from another material such as wood or clay. But cast iron is more brittle than wrought, as it hasn't been hammered.

Benchwork involves working on the cold metal with chisels, drills and other tools. Most locksmithery comes into this category; see p. 108.

Rust is important for two reasons; its absence can help to identify the metal, and its presence means instant repairs are in order. Rust is not just unsightly, it eats the metal.

Small ferrous pieces used at home can be kept clean by careful washing; if not used directly for food, a thin film of Vaseline or linseed oil will keep them in perfect condition.

1. I have seen many objects in cast iron, but I had never seen a cast-iron hand mirror before.

It might have been made for the tropics where wood would be easily damaged by bugs, but more likely it was a demonstration piece showing off the mould-maker's ability.

The detail is quite extraordinary, the period is c.1870, and the price £25. A new discovery, one of the charms of antique fairs.

2. Tin is a friendly metal, easily stamped, cut and pierced. For centuries it has been useful in the kitchen. Watch out for new Mexican objects; very similar but lighter. This English candlestick, c.1880, £20.

4. Punch and Judy figures were very popular cast-iron doorstops. Punch comes in a variety of guises, once brightly painted. The modern preference for subtlety had convinced dealers to scrape off any traces and leave the figures dark. Now fashion is swinging back towards enjoying their original state. This standing Punch is unusual; with traces of red and green, c.1850, £95. Watch out for copies crudely painted in shiny enamel gloss, like gnomes.

3. A piece of sculpture, but concave, and after some discussion with an auction house expert, we decided it was a sample in iron for a moulded insertion, probably to go onto the centrepiece of a cabinet.

The signature was A. Peche. Dagobert Peche had a factory in Austria at the time; this plaque was probably made in Vienna, possibly by another family member. As they were known to make insets for furniture, the conclusion seems logical. C.1900, £80-90, perhaps more with additional research which could confirm the source.

Metalware

Non-ferrous metals include copper, lead, brass, pewter, bronze and its gilded form, ormolu. There are other metal materials and alloys which have come in and out of fashion from time to time, such as spelter, chromium plate and aluminium.

COLLECTORS' NOTES

Traditional antique pewter is relatively soft because of its high lead content and it acquires bumps and dents very easily.

New pewter pieces in classic styles have been made for some time; those from France are particularly beautiful, but they are carefully marked and identified. Watch out for bruising on the base which might indicate a destroyed punchmark, and for the lack of that deep silver glow which antique pewter holds so well.

Bronze, an alloy of copper and tin, spelter and lead were often used for outdoor statuary and urns. The greeny-brown patina of bronze is highly treasured. Check by rubbing gently under the base with a damp cloth - artificial painting or patinas will come away.

Ormolu, or gilded bronze, is usually found on porcelain and furniture. 19th century lamps often had ormolu bases and handles, while fine French furniture was hinged, handled and keyed in ormolu for extra glitter.

Spelter is a cheap substitute for bronze, made with zinc. It was used for figures and decorative bits, but it is now respectable and reasonable in price. Lead was used generously in garden ornaments, but with few exceptions for a lucky find, they are now beyond our budget.

Chromium plating was the darling of the Deco designers; perhaps it was the association with fast cars that made chrome into the perfect partner with the right sort of image. It was also cheap, so it could be applied to leather bag clasps as well as bedheads, standard lamps, ashtrays, glove boxes, cigarette cases and so on.

1. Animal sculptures were an obsession with many 19th century collectors. Look for signatures or factory marks to make the best investment, but be prepared to pay more for that assurance. Here's one to take a flyer on: a bronze bird, unmarked, but of fine detail in the casting; c.1870, £75.

2. Bronze and enamel cap lifter, Portuguese, 1950s. £3. Not all bronze is from famous artists. A tourist souvenir in national colours, but made of genuine bronze metal.

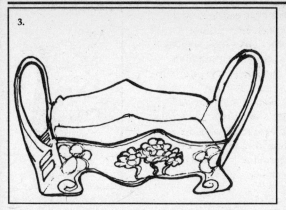

3. A small Art Nouveau fruit dish, cast pewter, made and stamped by the Orivit Company of Germany, c.1900. The pewter has been alloyed to make a very hard surface with a bronzed colouring. The featured handles are surprisingly delicate, and must have been quite difficult to keep from breaking out of the mould. The dish probably had a glass lining of some sort; having a lining made is neither difficult nor expensive, but choose the colour carefully to avoid distraction from the over-all impression of bronze.

A piece like this is more valuable because it embodies the Art Nouveau style so well; the scrolled feet, the drawn-out handles, and the raised, flowing design of the grapes on the side. Found for £9, current value at auction, £60-70.

5. Just as the pewter dish is the epitome of Art Nouveau, so this table lamp is Art Deco, complete in itself.

Everything is there; the circles and geometric shapes, the basic construction finished in bright chrome plating, the whole topped with spinning circles of pink, acid-etched glass.

With style like this, it's a shame to be practical, but there's no doubt that the wiring dates from the same period, and re-wiring is an absolute priority. Otherwise the lamp is in perfect condition, except for a small patch of chrome on the base which has begun to peel slightly. Treat it by cleaning off any flecks very carefully and coating with a layer of lacquer. C.1925, £75-85.

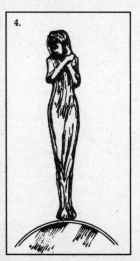

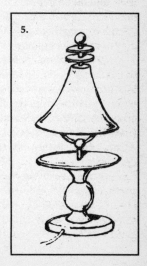

4. The aluminium handle of a magnifying glass, caught between the Art Nouveau curves and the simplified figurines of Art Deco. And probably a marriage in another sense as well.

Magnifying glasses are enjoying a vogue; you can see whole tables of them at the larger markets. Unfortunately some stall-holders find suitable designs of all periods to become handles.

This one may well have started life as the handle of a lady's dressing table mirror. £15.

115

Militaria

The experience of war has been reflected in the paraphernalia which accompanies it. Badges and models, uniforms and other relics of past glory and past horror, too. It's seldom soldiers and sailors who become militaria collectors; perhaps they are too near the real thing to want to remember. But there are also those who are fascinated by the strategy of war, who play endless war games as if it were chess, with battalions of toy soldiers and huge tables of topography where the great battles of the past can be re-enacted.

COLLECTORS' NOTES

This is perhaps the only area of collecting where guidelines of condition is reversed; there have been so many fakes that uniforms or articles showing signs of wear and tear are usually considered more authentic and therefore more attractive to the collector than mint-bright objects. Also, most of the collector's zeal goes with the people who wore or carried the object rather than its intrinsic worth as art.

It's also a nationally oriented field. In Britain, foreign uniforms, medals or decorations are far less valuable than ours, just as Civil War mementos in America take the top prices.

Look especially for any documentation or diaries or papers of any kind that might come with whatever you are buying. First because of that personal touch mentioned above, but also because there have been so many reconstructed war mementos for plays, films, TV programmes and even play-acting games for children that almost all claims are regarded with a certain amount of suspicion and supporting evidence is very helpful.

There are no arms and armour because the prices nowadays just can't be met within our budget, but the occasional knife or dagger may be affordable. Small objects like trench art from World War I, do come to the market from time to time, but they must be judged individually.

1. An embroidered regimental badge from Suffolk, now disbanded and absorbed into one of the larger units. A local collector might be very proud of such a memento. However, badges are the most easily faked of all militaria and unfortunately the fashion for youngsters sewing badges on their leather jackets has created a whole industry of copies and even imaginary regimental crests! You'll have to bone up on army history to really know what to buy.

In general, authentic badges of brass, or gilt and silver plate, sometimes on a velvet backing, are around £90-100, depending on their rarity and reasonable condition.

With letters or records as we mentioned before, add another £25. Hallmarked silver badges from 1900-1930 are quite common and sell for just a little more.

Badges were worn on the caps, on sleeves, on belts and on puggarees (a scarf wrapped around the head and falling on the neck as protection against the sun).

2. This trio of medals was affectionately called "Pip, Squeak and Wilfred" after a comedy team of the period. They were awarded after World War I to Driver Fell of the Royal Fusiliers, and include the 1914-1915 Star, the Victoria Medal, and the War Medal.

None are particularly rare, and so although the owner would have been dis-mayed, they will bring relatively little, about £40.

Medals are a very complex subject, and depend a great deal on the recipient, his fame, or on the battle or expedition for which they were awarded. As an example, there were twenty-two medals struck for Shackleton's Polar Expedition, 110 Conspicuous Gallantry Medals for World War I, and these both bring many thousands when they come on the market.

But a general service medal of 1848 might only bring £300. Research and reading are required for the collector.

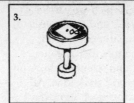

3. Shades of James Bond - this collar stud contains a working compass for air crew members of World War II, shot down over Europe, so they could try and find their way home. There are no statistics of how many crew members found it helped them, or whether it was simply discarded along with their uniforms, but such ingenious devices make a more pleasant memento of wartime than many.

4. The Spitfire retains its hold on the imagination. No other plane has ever symbolised a nation's trials so well, and everything associated with it brings a rush of nostalgia. This clock from a Spitfire would be worth more if it were documented as coming from a particular plane, whose record could be traced. As it is, only £29 for a piece of history which must be unique.

5. The Royal Air Force is an organisation which instills in its members an everlasting loyalty. Air Force pilots had the kind of glamour given only to screen heroes, and all their accoutrements have become symbolic of heroism, cool courage and devil-may-care gallantry. A lot to read into leather jackets with fur collars and these soft leather goggles. But the remaining few genuine articles have been so imitated and copied that absolute care is required. This pair, 1940s, came with a traceable name inside, so £60.

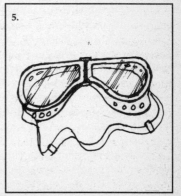

Miniatures

Tiny things have an appeal which we can recall vividly from *Gulliver's Travels* and *Midsummer Night's Dream*. Antique miniatures, in silver, ivory, wood or ceramics help perpetuate our sense of wonder that anything so small can be an accurate reflection of the world we know. All miniatures are collectable; the most coveted are those which move or work in some way.

COLLECTORS' NOTES

Have a magnifying glass with you all the time. It's useful for everything: marks, minute cracks or chips, glaze lines, fine details - all are only visible at close quarters and the success (or failure) of craftsmanship will be evident at once.

Although similar at first glance, there is a substantial difference between doll furnishings made for children and miniatures made for adults. The joint of a doll's chair is usually like two matchsticks crudely glued together, while a miniature in silver or carved rosewood may be as well made as your own. Naturally there are degrees of difference, and display furniture for magnificent dolls' houses are another matter.

A working miniature is valuable, but if it is not in good order, be cautious and careful unless you feel sure you can find an expert to give it proper attention. Amateur enthusiasm is not enough when one dig from the point of the wrong tool can shatter a glass or a cup.

Sometimes miniatures have been taken off charm bracelets; there was a great vogue in the 1940s and 1950s for elaborate, rotating windmills, books that open, fire engines with expanding ladders...most can be identified by the little ring for attaching to the links. Gold charms may not be too expensive and the stones are likely to be real. Silver charms are generally not so interesting, as they were mass-produced and the designs can be banal.

Display is important; keep your miniatures together, not scattered amongst larger things or the sense of scale becomes distorted.

1. Catholic travellers often carried a miniature communion set, here each piece carved from ivory and set in silver and in a silver (unmarked) box. Check that every piece is there - the value drops by half if even one of the candlesticks is broken. Remember, too, the law in many countries now prohibits trading in ivory less than 150 years old, so resale may be difficult. C.1865, possibly Indian, £75.

2. A tiny cup and saucer of hand-painted and gilded porcelain; no mark, probably French or Russian; c.1900, £12.

3.

3. The Romans lit their homes at night with pottery oil lamps of this shape; the wick was pulled through the spout to be set alight. Many, like this silver miniature model, had a cap to keep the dust out of the fuel. Hallmarked 1835, it has clearly been made with classical flair as its twisted and beautifully detailed snake handle shows. Made appropriately enough, albeit a millenium later, in Roman Chester; £75.

4. and 5. Silver wirework miniatures, woven painstakingly in a basketweave to represent a willow arbour seat and a matching table. Every bit is made by hand, and the only thing missing for your comfort might be a little cushion. Miniatures like this, obviously unique and individual, bring a premium but the lack of a mark makes it just a little less expensive. It's easy to see from the weaving that this is sterling silver, not plate, but many inexperienced buyers need the reassurance. English or German, c.1910-1920, £75.

6. Miniature chests of drawers are an instant success at any fair. They range from the most sophisticated serpentine shape in fine veneer to square country boxes in pine, thrown together by the local joiner to hold keys or pins.

This one comes somewhere in between; the wood is pine, but uniformly faded to a soft brown and polished until it glows. Round wooden handles like sourballs are repeated on the feet. A gently moulded top sits above all.

Look inside the drawers to see that they fit well, to make sure there's no newly cut wood, and to check that the handles are original. Look for a pleasant size, noting that the handles are always just a little large in proportion to the drawers.
C.1875, £55-75.

4.

5.

6.

Mirrors and Frames

*Mirror, mirror on the wall...*They date back as far as history goes, generally of polished bronze or steel, in small sizes just big enough to see one's face. Metal mirrors of all kinds have been found throughout the world. From the 16th century, glassmakers were able to create larger and larger pieces, as methods of making plate glass were tried out with varying degrees of success. A thin coating of mercury on one side turned the glass into a mirror.

Finally, in 1835, a German chemist developed the process of silvering mirror, which was safer, quicker and far less hazardous to health. Within a few decades, every kind of mirror was made in England and other countries; what was once a luxury was now a matter of everyday furnishing.

COLLECTORS' NOTES

Tall, narrow pier mirrors are characteristic of the neo-classical period, hanging between windows. The frames are narrow, usually with a larger band of decoration at the top.

Victorian over-mantles were generously sized, broader than high, often with integral shelves on either side so that treasured possessions could be reflected in the mirror and doubled in display value. Until recently these were thought heavy and cumbersome, but now fashion has given them a new lease of life and good examples are correspondingly very expensive. House clearance sales are your best source for reasonable prices.

Old glass gets cloudy and speckled with grey, as the backing wears away; unless it makes the mirror unusable, don't have it resilvered. The flecking is part of the attraction for collectors.

More modern mirrors rely on their frames for appeal. Cheap but decorative old picture frames can be mirrored and sold as originals. Any bright, exceptionally clear mirror is a modern piece. Hand mirrors from dressing table sets abound; watch out for marriages, with old knife-handles attached to new mirrored tops.

1. and **2.** Swing mirrors on dressing tables are an English tradition of the past hundred years; walk down the village street and see their backs in almost every upstairs window. However, finding good ones nowadays is not easy; the tide of fashion turned in the 1970s, leaving us with surprisingly few older examples of decent workmanship on the market.

You will find many similar to **1.**, a late Victorian version of a popular Georgian design. It was made in mahogany or painted pine; oak ones would have different legs.

Look for good wood with a pleasant patina, not the heavy gloss finish of the 1950s. Compare the side pieces with the outline - they should be sturdy but not heavy. Check the swing ratchets; cracks in the wood often start there if the mirror has been replaced. £85. With a drawer beneath, especially desirable, but probably over £100.

The second example, **2.**, is thirty years later. Open supports have been replaced by a geometric frame in limed oak with moulded decoration. There is seldom a drawer. The liming leaves the grain of the wood proud of the surface, and it has no patina, even after sixty years, but the wood can be waxed and polished. C.1935, £45-65.

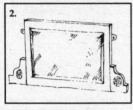

4. Victorian mirrors in plush frames are hard to find. The velvet wore out before wood or metal, so they were probably thrown away. Some small frames survive but these larger ones with matching shelf are rare. Watch out for bare cloth patches, painted over to disguise them. Steam very gently to restore the plush. C.1875-85 £75 in good condition; don't buy otherwise.

3. Art Deco motifs reached every level; austere, sharp geometrics for Cartier jewellery, coy dancing girls for the High Street. This lady with a round mirror could not be more typical; no collector of kitsch should be without it. Unmarked pottery, c.1935, £35.

5. The glamour of a golden past. This Rococo style is a 1930s' copy, with its London store label still intact. The wood is carved, the gold leaf is well laid; this is reproduction of the better kind, and with enough age to give it some character. £45.

6. Peach glass with frosted picture. Even the chrome clips are original. Almost a museum piece. C.1932, £25.

Mirrors and Frames

Picture frames have a long history - early miniatures were set in precious frames, embellished with enamelled flowers and scattered with jewels. The Georgians preferred classical mouldings taken from architectural originals. The Victorians created generous frames, often larger than the painting, with the occasional flower or cupid tucked in a corner.

All such frames now cost hundreds and even thousands of pounds. However, the budget collector can still find a substantial number of affordable photograph frames.

The first photographs were taken by artists experimenting with fragile equipment; their work in the 1840s and 1850s was usually stored in protective cabinets. Even when photography became widespread, taking family portraits was a twice-in-a-lifetime event. With Kodak (see Cameras) all that changed. Outings and holidays were recorded by snapshots, and individual frames were overshadowed by massive photographic albums, the new family bibles.

The pendulum swung back with the Art Deco and Hollywood, when signed photos were displayed on stage and screen sets. If you couldn't quite manage Theda Bari (or a Princess) then Auntie Jessie would have to do.

COLLECTORS' NOTES

Small frames, especially in silver, are extremely collectable. Look for hallmarks or trademarks to help date them. Their popularity has had the unfortunate result that a huge number of designs are now being reproduced, and market stalls can be covered in new stamped-silver tops on Victorian plush backings.

Brass frames, without marks, are harder to date. Thin, single-strut supports are earlier than the wider triangles which fold into the backing. Look for the fine detail of the late Georgian period, and the nature designs of mid-century Victorians. Corners resoldered or badly joined give away poorly done repairs.

1. This pewter alloy frame dates from the Victorian period of preoccupation with natural forms. Ferns and bamboos were popular for decades and were applied to every possible surface. Later the images were copied onto ever-cheaper metal frames.

The design was stamped out of thin metal, and then pinned to a leathercloth-covered back. Many finds like this still retain their photographs.

Stamped frames are not very strong, as the metal, thin enough for the process, is liable to bending and creasing, so if you have to remove it from the backing for any reason, do it very carefully.

Edwardian and later photograph frames are likely to be quite small; they stood on a table or the top of a piano.

Watch out for damaged stands, often just folded card. They have to be repaired very neatly or it affects the value. C.1920, £25 for a pair.

2. Oval frames are fairly common from the 18th century on.

The earliest were made for portraits or silhouettes. These will be thicker, and the whole back comes off to give access to the surround.

From the time photographs became common (1880s), a slit in the top of the frame was used. Each one here, £55.

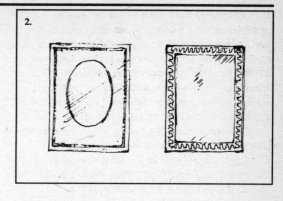

3. Silver frames are still reasonably affordable, although unusual and/or heavy examples bring quite a lot of money. This curtained example is exactly that; beautifully detailed with moulded borders and the added value of an original curtained front in reasonable condition. These were often used for miniatures of deceased relatives; this one has been replaced with a mirrored back. 1865, £95.

4. Two ceramic frames of the 1930s, with various designs. These are still made today, so look for period designs and hand painting.

Souvenir frames were made with legends from seaside towns on them, much sought by collectors.

Modern frames will be thickly potted and heavy. Pairs are uncommon - be prepared to pay more than twice as much.
£20 each if singles, £55 if a matching pair.

5. Photograph albums began to appear in Victorian times. They were very elaborate confections, and became treasured family possessions.

This 1875 album still has its black pages half filled with family snapshots which go up to 1910.

If you must, take out old photographs with a great deal of care . The paper tears so easily, and then crumbles into shreds. £40. If mounted with silver, £80.

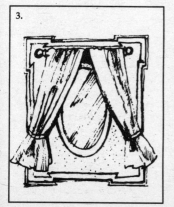

Ornaments

Many objects which we think of as purely ornamental once had a genuine function, now lost, or more often unrecognised. A great deal of kitchen equipment comes into this category, as well as personal possessions carried in pockets or handbags. Even with a portmanteau title like ornaments, there are additional examples elsewhere in the text, in brass, pottery and so on.

A definition, then, has to begin with having no purpose except to amuse or please the eye. Although we regard the Victorians as great ornamentalists for its own sake, every period has had its share; objects treasured only for themselves have been around for as long as society has had time to do more than find food, shelter and warmth.

COLLECTORS' NOTES

The finest ornaments are charming or interesting subjects, in harmony with their material. Indeed, since they have no other purpose, the combination of craft and structure is paramount.

Look at the detail; in porcelain, the edges should be clearly defined, the painting subtle and well executed, the outlines crisp. In pottery, the pattern is often simpler, the painting cruder, the outlines thicker to suit the clay.

Royal Doulton porcelain figurines are a story in themselves, and there are precise guides to when each model was produced, who designed it and what each model brings and why. The guides are essential reading if you are interested in that field, as over 200 models are still in production.

Less well known are Grimswade and Birks Rawlings & Co, both of whom made porcelain figures of interesting designs in the 1920s and 1930s. Art porcelain of this period is a relatively new field, too, and worth investigating.

Continental factories of the 20th century produced a great many unmarked pieces; most are impossible to identify without additional clues, but the different bodies and glazes will help your search for information.

1. The image of the nymph in a seashell is older than Botticelli's Venus, and it occurs over and over again. However, this little 1920s girl is so small she fits neatly into your hand. It is her modelling that gives her age and provenance away. Slim and short-haired, with the headband of the twenties, the skill in making the figurine is typical of one of the German factories in the 1920s or 1930s. The very white body and thin lustre glaze support that date, too.

She is set inside a lustre shell of beige and pearl and her tunic may once have been gilded - there are traces here and there. It's amazing that not a single one of her extremely delicate and outstretched fingers or toes is missing.

Watch out for such small damaged areas; they are very hard to see in such a miniature piece, yet they would bring her value down from £55 to £25.

If marked, it might well double the value, too.

1.

2. In the 1920s and 1930s, Germany provided novelty ornaments for the world, especially "naughty" models of young girls. Some looked dressed from the front but were naked at the back, or had no clothes at all, and some like this little girl on a potty, were distinctly schoolboyish humour. Socially interesting, and more value if in a related group for a cost of £15-20.

4. Hands have obsessed collectors - this Victorian example is particularly charming. The shell bowl is light lustre, with ribbed beige. Unmarked, probably English, £55.

3. Ornamental figurines have been made for centuries; the most popular buys are the naive 18th and 19th century Staffordshire fairings, and the Doulton figurines, still designed and made today in limited editions.

Both are usually over our limit, although some of the everyday models can be found from time to time. And both have been quite heavily faked, with crude colours and, in the case of the Doulton figures, poor potting and awkward modelling.

Happily we are beginning to recognise some smaller potters working in the 1920s and 1930s, producing attractive pieces at still-affordable prices. This little governess or school-teacher in lavender blue, with her books piled up, is both charming and well made. The mark is Tuscan China, c.1930s, £90.

More elaborately painted figures are now bringing £140 and up.

5. A friend began a swan collection a year ago; eight months later she repented, as she sank under the weight of their feathers.

This very large swan in white porcelain is one of the better ones, finely potted with feathered plumage, black and red beak, and a yellow eye. Marked Booth's, c.1938, £55. Not known before from this factory.

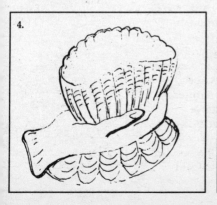

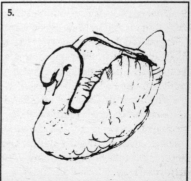

Ornaments

The huge output of newly industrialised countries in the 19th century flooded the world, when factories and workshops turned out batches of metal models in quantities that couldn't have even been imagined twenty years before. The other discouraging factor for the collector in search of information was the growth of major transport systems, taking, for example, bronzes from Austria to every corner of globe, for sale in shops as far apart as Brazil and Australia. Between these two economic changes, the difficulties of being sure about attribution and source have increased a hundred-fold.

COLLECTORS' NOTES

Every possible material has been used at one time or another to make ornaments. There may be nothing, not even a mark or a number, to help you find the history of your particular object. Try to keep every scrap of information - the name on a box, the remains of a label, the dealer's tag; ask for any knowledge or even educated guess the dealer might make and write it down.

Some collectors rely too much on registration marks - that little diamond which contained date and year letters. At least it assures you the object was registered in Britain, but it is only the date of the design registration, not of manufacture. The diamond was used from 1842-1883, but popular designs could be continued for decades, and some ceramic patterns are still being used. Registered Numbers continued with roughly 20,000 new registrations every year.

Registered Trade and Patent Marks are also slightly misleading for the same reason; they give you the first date the object could have been made, but not when it was actually produced.

The American Tarif Act of 1891 required imports to bear their country of origin. Please see Glossary, and look under Dating, for more detail.

Learning more about a subject and the craft is still the best way of identifying your bargain discoveries.

1. A tiny bird breaking out of its shell. For collectors of ivory it would have been a charming little amusement but scarcely a major piece, not because of the size, but because it is fundamentally very simple. It isn't Japanese, but probably made in Dieppe c.1850-1880; the bird is silver-gilt, with a French mark.

During most of the 19th century, until it was occupied by the Prussian army in the 1870s, Dieppe was the major European centre for ivory carving.

It was also a huge tourist market, made popular by the English on their way to the Continent who stopped to buy trinkets and so on from the Dieppoise, who produced them in quantity. They worked in family groups, some of which continued to operate until very recently when the outcry against the use of ivory made their profession less and less profitable.

Our little chick is so tiny that the famous Dieppoise signature of very intricate work is missing. They also made toys, games, model boats, chess sets, boxes and all sorts of decorative knick-knacks. £95.

2. A miniature toby jug of , bronze, cold painted, and bright silvered balls on the collar. No signature, but there is a number on the base. The most likely source is Austrian, around the turn of the century when a number of factories turned out all sorts of bronzes, especially animals, and joky figures like this jug. C.1890-1910, £85.

3. Chinese carved wood standing figures have a long list of avid collectors searching for the best specimens. For those of lesser means, there are newer pieces, especially those carved in the early 20th century for the first of the mass-market tourist trade. The crafts-men still paid a lot of attention to detail; this god has a little monkey at his feet. A minefield of reproduction, so do your homework. C.1920s, hardwood, £55.

4. Dog figures were so popular that by the end of the 19th century they were being made in substantial numbers. While early pairs of ceramic dogs are rare and covetable, this one is later, single, in painted iron and within our budget. The back has a plate for pulling off your boots. Look for features like its gilded collar. Modern copies are too bright, and the painting will be blotched,and run at the edges. C.1880, £95.

5. In 1959, *Ben Hur* was remade starring Charlton Heston. The chariot race was considered the greatest action sequence produced for modern films, and this metal model of a chariot and Heston, with moving wheels and loose harness chains, was a souvenir. Heston's shirt in the film sold this year for £450. Hollywood is new to antique hunters; research your finds to give them some authority. An advertisement for this model would raise the price from £15 to £50, and a note or photo showing it being given away at the premiere might bring that to £500 or more.

Pens and Pencils

Inkstands and inkwells are an accepted part of antique history. They are represented in a separate section because of their fascinating variety, but they have been largely replaced on our desks by the modern tools of writing, fountain pens and pencils. While early plumed pens have been collected for years, the more modern pen and pencil have only recently joined the collectables club. Not surprisingly, since fountain pens were invented in America, collecting started there, and has become interesting to British collectors (and therefore to market and stall holders) only recently.

The problem will be one of selection rather than search; so many kinds, marks, models and materials were used that the new collector needs a handbook or memory organiser to carry with them. Now when they start collecting those...

COLLECTORS' NOTES

The fountain pen story begins with Louis Waterman, whose patent was taken out as long ago as 1884. The idea was such a success that in four years there were at least fifty known models on sale, and ten years later Parker joined the fray. These two, together with Schaeffer, all American and all still making pens, dominate the market.

The early plain pens were soon being decorated in luxurious materials, but most of the pens available to us at a reasonable cost are from the 1920s and 1930s, with a few later models coming up fast. An original box is a great asset.

With rare exceptions, plain black pens are not very valuable unless they represent an unusual model; prices can be as little as £7 or £8. On the other hand, coloured examples of early Parkers fetch £200-400, while lacquered Dunhill pens of the 1920s, designed by Japanese artists, can bring over £1,000.

Ink sacs can be replaced, but watch carefully for splits in the shaft, replaced nibs and mis-matched caps. Some dealers hold stocks of caps only.

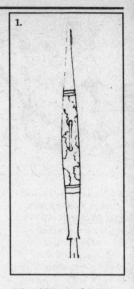

1. In addition to fountain pens for the pocket and handbag, Waterman and the other manufacturers made a range of desk pens, and often worked together with designers and studios to produce desk sets, blotters, rollers, and so on. A feature was the pen holder on a swivel bearing which held the pen ready for use.

These generally slim pens are often highly decorated to match the rest of the set.

Look for the complete set, or at least the matching pen holder. Desk pens alone are nowhere near as valuable.

The nib can be damaged from pushing down into the holder - examine it carefully. This 1930s white ripple pen alone, £18. In its holder, £45.

2. A selection with interesting patterns or finishes. Left to right, a Parker Shadow Wave Vacumatic pencil, c.1939, £40. For some reason pencils have never brought the same kind of money as their matching pens. Strange, because the case is just the same, and the mechanism of most of these mid-century pens is quite standard. However, it offers some interesting possiblities for the collector willing to take a chance on future value.

Look for working pencils, unscrew them to make sure the lead holder is undamaged. One advantage is that without a nib, there is less of a possibility of it being a marriage between an old body and new parts. Do check that the cap matches, though.

The next is a silver propelling pencil; these were made in great numbers from as early as the 1830s and 1840s. Most are well under £100, with just a few novelties tipping over the limit. A magnificent collection can be built up quite quickly. Samson Mordan & Co of London made the best; this slim one, £45.

Next, the 1936 Onoto Pen, by De La Rue & Co. with a pleasant textured finish. £95. 1910s silver filigree models of this pen can fetch up to £900. Fourth, a Parker 51, that standard graduation gift

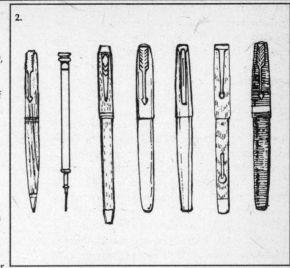

with a stainless steel cap, £20. Next, a fat Waterman of 1968, a bargain at £18.

Then the famous Mont Blanc 42, even fatter, c.1950, £50, and after that a Parker Streamline Duofold Special from 1929, £70.

While an ordinary Duofold of this period might be as little as £7-9, this one has a lovely lacquer-red ripple case, and it's in its original box with the receipt.

3. A man with an eye to the future was our artist's father, who was given this first "edition" of the Biro, the Biro De Luxe of 1958.

Mr. Robb elected to keep it in its original box, proudly announcing the beginning of an era.

Of course Dr Biro's name has become part of the English language, and this boxed example of the very first production run is now worth £50 or more.

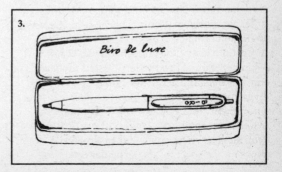

Biro De luxe

Plastics

Twenty-five years ago I saw a proposal for a book called the *Encyclopedia of Plastic Antiques* rejected out of hand. Remembering that plastics may well have resulted in some mass-produced horrors, we can replay now that so did Victorian brassworks.

COLLECTORS' NOTES

The first vulcanised rubber was made in 1840s America, and intended for car tyres. The same substance, hardened with additional sulphur, made a shiny black material called Vulcanite in Britain. It was quite popular for jewellery in place of jet, for hair combs and boxes, pens, candlesticks, etc.

The next collectable plastic is Parkesine - also invented in the 1840s here, and made in an ivory colour and a tawny, tortoiseshell brown. Seldom recognised, Parkesine is rare - the company had already closed in c.1870. Celluloid (a trade name now commonly used for a material) began production in the same year, and this is easy to find, affordable and fascinating. And very inflammable, so keep any pieces in cool rooms.

Bakelite is now a familiar word to collectors, invented here by Mr Baekeland; it was the first real resin. Colours remained dark - blacks, browns, red, greens and blues. Bakelite was the darling of 1920s Art Deco designers.

These early plastics were created in sheets. In the mid-1920s, the first moulded tablewares were made, sprinkled with colours while still in liquid form, and the result created some new and amazing marble patterns. This became the major material of domestic use, as Bandalasta, and almost the last of the craft-made plastics.

Huge machine production created thousands of various plastic articles, developed to suit our hygienic and disposable lifestyle. Plastic lost its excitement and became a word synonomous with cheap and nasty. Only now are artists treating acrylics in particular as a material worthy of respect for its particular qualities.

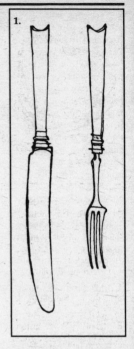

1. A dessert set in silver, hallmarked 1904, with delicate Bakelite handles in dark green, their edges beautifully carved out into points.

The forks and knives are unusually slender and elegant, which gives them their instant appeal.

The Bakelite has been scratched a little presumably in use, but not a single tip is broken. Laid on a table, the complete set makes a wonderful appearance.

Avoid making any additional scratches by making sure they aren't dumped into a drawer with other sharp-edged cutlery. £65 the set for six.

2. Celluloid tortoiseshell bag handle, inlaid with mother of pearl. The bag itself is in good condition, and the chain is unbroken. C.1900, £55.

3. This radio could have been made in the 1930s, but in fact it was a Murphy model of 1946. The fluted edges of the speaker give it away; earlier models would have plain, cut-out openings. But its shape and size are very similar. £35.

4. Bandalasta was a remarkable success, with exhibitions at Harrod's to show off its modern look. Marbling could now be linked to brilliant colours, and Bandalasta and its competitors were made in yellow, blue, amber, red and green. Bandalasta is marked; Shellware is another trade name. This teapot, 1930s, £25. A contemporary Bandalasta catalogue will show you the shapes.

5. A manicure set in a green Bakelite box with artificial silk lining and all the required implements with matching Bakelite handles.

When buying a set like this missing pieces are very important as the value will plummet if even one implement is gone. Sets are still around in reasonable quantity, so the prices are reasonable, too, but complete ones are being snapped up. £22.

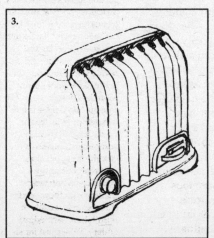

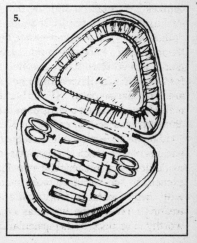

Porcelain

The very word has come to mean delicate, smooth and fragile, yet porcelain is the most durable and the toughest of all ceramics. Its ability to take fine moulding and clear colourings has given craftsmen the raw material to create some of the most beautiful objects of all time.

COLLECTORS' NOTES

Porcelain is made from china clay, a particularly fine substance from the earth. In the world of antiques, it is sub-divided into soft paste, hard paste, and bone china.

The original development of porcelain took place in China, where the clay was mixed with a unique mineral called petunse, or china stone. Any object formed or modelled in porcelain clay, and baked in a high-temperature kiln becomes a hard, impermeable material, cold to the touch, tough and glassy, with a very smooth finish. The object is decorated, glazed and fired again at a lower temperature. Later, gilding and bright enamel colours were added to the repertoire on top of the glaze.

When European potteries of the 17th century tried to make porcelain, they had neither china clay nor china stone; the nearest they achieved was soft paste. Soft paste is weak and easily damaged, the glaze is difficult to control, and production was gratefully abandoned when the right kind of clay and china stone deposits were discovered in various places in Europe, making it possible to produce a very credible alternative to the Chinese ware. This became known as hard paste, or true porcelain. The collector on a budget will seldom find soft paste pieces now; even damaged ones are expensive.

In England, Josiah Spode was the first to add bone ash to the china clay (c.1795) and during the great expansion of the 19th century, it was adopted by other English factories, who have continued to manufacture it until the present day. In the rest of the world only America took up the formula for its own porcelain industry.

1. This small English tureen dates from some time in the 1890s. Its dark blue bands have a gold leaf pattern. The size makes it very useful, and with an elegant shape and a perfect lid it's a desirable piece.

Lack of a mark does count against it, but that doesn't necessarily mean poor quality. Many good factories did not mark every piece in a dinner or tea service, which makes it difficult to be sure of attribution when the service is broken up.

Dishes which should have had lids will cost less when the lid is missing, unless the pattern is rare or unusually attractive. Watch out for the little ridge, usually inside the rim which may indicate whether or not there was a cover originally.

Look for quality of execution in how the pattern has been fitted to the shape, particularly when the body is double curved as this is. It can tell the expert a great deal about which factories would - or would not - be likely to produce such a comparatively sophisticated design.

Watch out for hairline cracks around the knob and under the base. See that the lid fits well - a rattling lid usually means a misfired piece. Watch out for small chips, which are harder to spot in porcelain because of the white body. £45-50.

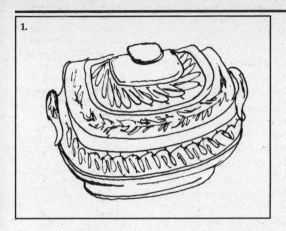

1.

2. Toast racks are a fruitful field for collectors because they were made in so many designs and by so many companies. This little fan toast rack is typical of Continental styles in the late 19th century. The porcelain modelling is not particularly fine, but the body is a clear glassy white with a pleasantly clear glaze, too. The edges are gilded. Continental, no mark, c.1870, £35-40.

3. A Bodley 1880s dessert set of three octagonal compotes and five plates; brilliant turquoise borders with four hand-painted landscapes of imaginary scenes on each piece.

Any hand painting is worth attention, for study if nothing else. Colours used by the porcelain decorators have to be judged by experience, as firing in the high-temperature kiln changes them.

The border is edged with a gilded bamboo pattern which has worn slightly in places. The feet are shaped like trunks of trees, typical of the naturalistic period.

I had owned this set for over thirty years and had never seen another. Last year I decided to sell it, and that same evening an identical set was brought in to a fellow dealer for double the money. We all make mistakes. No chips or cracks; some fading on the centres. £45 each compote, £30 each plate.

2.

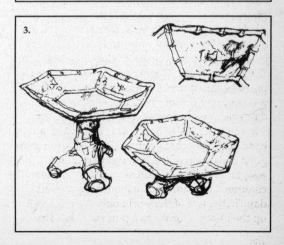

3.

Porcelain

By the end of the 19th century, porcelain on the Continent and bone china in England had become the standard ceramic ware for the finest decorative pieces and for the best tableware. England was the predominant manufacturer of ceramic wares and English designs were admired throughout the world. However, as the Arts and Crafts movement took hold, artists turned back to earthenware, which seemed to embody the ideal of the mediaeval potter. Bone china, by now the standard English product, began to lose its sharp edge and through the first part of the 20th century, with rare exceptions, English bone china design was repetitive and weakly traditional. More exciting developments were happening in earthenware and on the Continent.

COLLECTORS' NOTES

Porcelain, including bone china, is translucent - when you hold up a plate to the light you can see the shape of your fingers. When lightly struck it has a clear ring unless it is cracked, and painted enamel decoration stays proud of the surface.

The glaze and the body on porcelain clay fuse in the kiln. Any chipped edges will be sharp-edged and glossy, very like glass.

Bone china is slightly creamier in colour than Continental porcelain, so that the body is never quite as white. A mark which includes Bone China or English Bone China is 20th century. "England" alone means it is post 1891, when American law required all imports to state their country of origin. Not all ceramics were marked like that since it only applied to those pieces intended for the US.

Restoration of porcelain is quite common nowadays, as many people have learned to do it at home. Most dealers will tell you whether or not a piece has been restored. Watch out for the signs - a slight roughening of the surface, a little bump on a thin edge, a very slight area of discolouration.

1. A teacup and saucer from a set for eight. The design is little bunches of roses with gilded edges; not very original, but the roses are sparse enough to make an open, fresh pattern. Rather more interesting is the shape of the cup, with an unusual little "rubber tyre" curve just above the base. I'd never seen this before, and there was no mark I could see on any of the pieces when I bought the set; the dealer didn't think there was one either, and the price was fair.

Once home I found an initialled sailing ship on just one of the cake plates. The best mark book for British potteries had it under "ships", and gave me a name for W.A.A.

When I sold the set on, it was properly attributed to the firm of Adderley's, and since the mark didn't include the full name of the firm, it was made during the period of the founder, William Alsager Adderley, who died in 1905. An example of how little known this period still is, even in the trade. Bought for £40, sold for £120.

2.

2. In 1904, Charles Ford was making some delightful pottery and porcelain, among which is this seashell teapot, its coral handle and branches, scrolled shells and shell base lovingly potted in pure white porcelain. Ford had a small pottery which started making crested china. He was bought out by a larger manufacturer, and his own style was gradually abandoned - he died in 1925. Ford is typical of the little-known makers a budget collector ought to look for; his work sells quite inexpensively because there are few who know his name, much less his work, and it has a charm and imagination of considerable quality. C.1904, £50.

3. One of a pair of fishy sauceboats, in the naturalistic style of the teapot above, although unmarked. Very attractive, and worth the investment of £65 for the pair and some time spent in research to see if they may be by Ford or a contemporary. C.1900.

4. This pretty porcelain dressing set is typical of Edwardian production; beautifully made and sensibly designed, but not very exciting. It harks back to the Victorians rather than looks forward to the 20th century. Nonetheless, there is everything a lady could want - from bottles and boxes to a tray and even a mirror painted with flowers. Its value today lies in its completeness rather than the design or the painting, even though both are acceptable quality. 1910, £95.

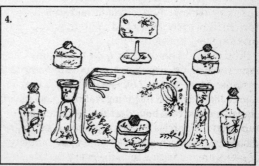

4.

3.

Porcelain

From the turn of the century, the making of porcelain and bone china body had become standardised to a very large degree. Even the varied shapes of plates and serving pieces had settled down to standard sizes and a kind of common ground throughout Europe. Those few companies which did take the plunge and develop really unusual shapes and new bodies found their market more secure as a result. Art Deco geometric plates, filled angular handles, and squared cups can be recognised at once, and like 18th century porcelain, be fairly confidently attributed to a particular factory or designer.

COLLECTORS' NOTES

Look for early 20th century work from the smaller factories, not yet widely appreciated, for unusual and potentially valuable pieces.

Art Deco porcelain is rarer than pottery of the same period. Well-known names like Clarice Cliff worked largely in earthenware and stoneware. Shelley was one of the few factories which used the new designs on porcelain.

Novelty porcelain of the 1920s and 1930s came (and comes today) largely from the Continent, Japan and China. Pottery was not acceptable to the Europeans unless it was traditional, like Quimper in France or Delftware from the Netherlands. Porcelain was preferred for souvenirs and trinkets as well as tableware and collectables. Most was not marked, and it was produced by dozens of small factories.

For art tableware, fashionable and stylish production in the 1960s and 1970s moved largely to Germany, France and Italy.

Today porcelain - and Britain - have come into their own again. Factories are more adventurous, and studio potters can buy kilns to reach the same high, controllable temperatures. Their work is pushing out the boundaries of the material, and serious porcelain collectors should be aware that some modern pieces and the work of many potters are increasing in value every decade.

1. The budget collector should investigate some of the smaller companies; Davenport is better known for its earthenware, but it made some very pleasant porcelain pieces. This cup and saucer has a good shape and an even better painting of rural vegetables and flowers. Looking at comparatively unknown factories will provide you with some unusual pieces for your collection at reasonable cost or better. This 1860s cup and saucer, £75.

Booth's produced some fine Worcester-style porcelains in the 1930s, and they are little known and well worth looking for at about £50 a beautifully decorated plate with fantastic birds.

Copeland is another factory which produced some good wares in the 1900s-1950s period.

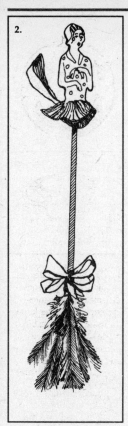

2. Too mad to ignore, this 1930s' pink feather duster with its porcelain handle is German; £12-15.

3. Parian ware is a matt porcellanous material used mainly for busts, statues and other marble look-alikes. This one of a pair of bookends with a sleepy child, unmarked, may be Minton, who made many fine Parian statues. If traced, the value would at least treble. £100.

4. and 5. Left, a fine Noritake Japanese set from a service in gold and green. 1950s, £15. Buy and put it away. More typical Noritake designs are more expensive. Below, Shelley 1930s' lobed cup and saucer; £55 for the trio. This period is collectable, but condition is vital.

Pottery

Although all ceramics are sometimes called pottery, to collectors it means earthenware or stoneware rather than porcelain. Earthenware is fired at a lower temperature than porcelain, the clay is not mixed with china stone, and it does not become fused with the glaze, but stays porous and distinct from its surface. The great variation in clay and glazes add to the possible confusion.

Potteries usually use local clays which can be white, grey, cream, pink or reddish. Regions and even individual factories can be identified this way, although not so easily when many worked in the same neighbourhood, as in the area of the Midlands known, quite simply, as the Potteries because of the many local factories.

COLLECTORS' NOTES

Pottery is often described by its glaze; delft and majolica are tin glazes which give an opaque, white surface, though the clay does show through where chips and cracks occur. English and Dutch delftware can be distinguished by the colour of their underlying bodies, as well as by decorative details.

Creamware, first developed by Wedgwood, has a transparent glaze over a fine, creamy body.

Other terms, such as slipware and spongeware, describe decoration. Slip is liquidised clay which is applied as a glaze, or in thin trails or three-dimensional designs, before glazing. Early English jugs were dipped in slip and then a pattern or design would be scratched through the slip to reveal the original colour. Spongeware has glaze patted on to give a distinctive open pattern, now very popular again in modern pottery.

Stoneware is fired at a higher temperature and becomes impervious to liquid even before it is glazed. It has been used for kitchen and shop utensils for centuries. Josiah Spode bought the patent for a new, finer stoneware which he named New China or Stone China; by 1813, Mason's Ironstone had appeared. Subsequent versions include Booth's Silicon China and similar names.

1. The outside rim of this soap dish curves to fit over a missing bowl. The central hole allows air to dry the soap. A similar perforated cress dish would have no central hole, and three lugs underneath to keep the dish away from a bottom plate. This Booth's soap dish from c.1880 in the traditional pink and blue colours of the Pagoda pattern; £22 for the top, £45 with its plain white bowl.

2. The willow pattern - perhaps the most famous of all pottery designs. Collect the infinite number of variations and read the specialised books to find the rarities. There is a similar pattern with no willow which is often mistaken for it. This large platter, c.1875, no mark, £35.

3. A few years ago, pot lids were very popular with collectors of small antiques. A large group could be displayed in one shallow tray, they were widely available and seemed infinitely variable. Today there's been a drop in general enthusiasm, so perhaps there is a greater possibility for the new collector to make some interesting finds.

Pot lids were largely made between 1848 and 1880 by one company, Pratt's of Fenton in Staffordshire. Later production went on in other factories until the 1900s. They were covers for small round pottery containers of hair grease; the pots were also used for foods like fish paste and potted shrimps.

The earliest lids were flat, printed with only two colours in an engraved picture, usually an adapted painting. Later the lids were slightly rounded with up to five colours.

Illustrations, which were surprisingly detailed, include portraits, landscapes, rural scenes and animals. Most were made without a name, although there are a few with the retail product engraved within the design. The majority had the contents and retailer added on a paper label. These two, £80 and £95 respectively. Pot lids have their own price guides (see Reference List).

5. Doulton made salt-glazed stoneware from the mid-19th century onwards. Their pottery at Lambeth was the heart of a salt-glaze revival, and by the turn of the century most others had been absorbed by Doulton's. Their building, now a business centre, still boasts the original tiles and terracotta panels on the exterior.

This jug shows the typical decoration of their stoneware range, which included coffee pots and mugs, as well as jugs in all shapes and sizes, but almost always with a wide-bellied bottom and a good, strong handle. The decoration is moulded or sprigged relief, the inside and top third glazed in dark brown. They are usually but not always marked. This one is, so £65. Some have silver mounts and might be £80 or more. Other factories as far away as Scotland also made brown saltglaze.

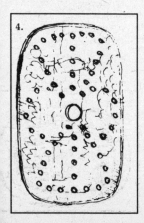

4. A meat drainer in a typical blue and white pattern. These were set inside large platters to allow the juices to be saved for the stock pot or gravy. Although once ignored unless complete with their platter, the piercing and flat shape has made them attractive as a display, and interesting patterns are now eagerly sought after. C.1890, £55. Well over £150 for a rare Mason's or Spode pattern.

Pottery

Dating from the mid-18th century, transfer printing was used extensively on pottery until early in the 20th century, when it was replaced by modern methods. The pattern is printed onto paper and transferred to the unglazed clay. The two general categories are printed designs finished in one colour and outline prints which were intended to be overpainted and then re-fired. Economically run potteries sometimes did both versions from one set of papers - plain for the cheaper market and painted for more expensive wares.

COLLECTORS' NOTES

The best production in single colours used quite complex patterns, such as landscapes or views taken from etchings or paintings, and these were not intended for overpainting. Quality can be judged not only in the artwork but in the care taken to set the transfer at the correct angle; hastily made wares can be spotted by overlap where the borders join or by the edges of patterns that drift off the piece.

Bat-printing was a technical development of the 18th century, where the transfer was made first onto a flexible film; this added to the accuracy in placement for the best wares.

Blue on white, inspired by Chinese porcelain, was produced with the easiest colour to fire - cobalt blue. It has remained an obsession with many collectors, but black, sepia, red and green were all used and these can make a really interesting collection, albeit more difficult to find.

There are literally thousands of designs; a collector needs a theme like a factory, birds, a series, etc. Matching up a service will increase the value of individual items considerably, but check the mark carefully. Popular designs were often bought, sold or copied, and a mixed-origin set is not as valuable, though it may make no difference to the fine appearance on your dresser or shelves.

1. A simple plate, with the simplest of blue and white patterns. The edge is called an arcade and it makes an unusual finish to an otherwise conventional pattern.

The plate is unmarked, but the light body and good finish put it early in the period, somewhere around 1810-1830.

Sometimes these have a slightly luminous glaze called pearlware, invented some time in the late 1700s when they discovered that adding a little extra blue to the transparent glaze made the white look whiter - we use eye brightener today for the same cosmetic effect. You can usually see the presence of blue in the thicker parts where the glaze has collected, under the rim.

These two elements, an early date and the pearlware, give this otherwise ordinary plate an extra value, bringing its price to something like £80-90. Finding matching pieces to build a set of something like this would be both unlikely and exciting.

2. A small blue and white jug with a landscape pattern. Potteries liked to include exotic scenes in their patterns, which gave them added appeal. This pagoda and jungle setting may have been taken from an engraving or from a chinese plate. Tracing the source might give this otherwise ordinary jug an extra fillip to the collector who enjoys research, and possibly added value if successful. £38, no mark, "46" on base.

4. An unidentified platter with a distinctive pattern in blue transfer and green lustre called "Etruscan" on the back. It may be by Pratt, but there is no mark. Be careful of marks set inside a discoloured patch - that usually means a fake mark. As is, this unusual dish, one of two, would bring £95 for the pair.

5. Here the blue transfer print has been over-painted in brilliant colours to make a pattern called Pagoda. Booth's produced a stoneware called Silicon China at the end of the 19th century, and continued to make it until the 1930s. Booth's made some very fine pottery using good colours and copies of excellent patterns. The mark has become extremely popular with collectors looking for something different, and within the past three years prices have trebled. Now about £45 for this pot-pourri or sugar basin, and rising fast.

3. Some blue and white is intentionally much paler than usual; this large platter has a slightly different kind of pattern, with a temple in the foreground and a riverside town in the background, made both in blue and white and in over-painting. There is no mark on this one, although an identical one has been recorded marked with the monogram of Thomas Dimmock's Stone China. That helps to suggest a date of 1840, and a probably price of £90. A marked platter might bring another £30 or £40.

Pottery

The greatest use we have always made of pottery has been in useful wares. Making attractive things that everyone needed was a profitable industry, and Victorian potteries had flourished. Most mid-19th century patterns followed the Chinese style, or the European versions of Chinese fashioned by Meissen and Dresden; then the great Victorian love of fulsome decoration took over; bouquets and floral delights proliferated at an alarming rate. But finally at the turn of the century, with the Arts and Crafts movement in particular, pottery finally came into its own as an art form as well as a useful craft.

Salt glaze and other rougher glazes became part of the back-to-nature movement, encouraged and inspired by Japanese tea wares with their subtle abstract patterns and thick dark colours. William Morris, Ruskin, William de Morgan and many other artists began to work with clay; the impetus moved away from large factories and into small workshops. The group of reformers went on to include world-famous potters such as Bernard Leach, and it's known up the 1930s as Art Pottery, and from then until the present time as Studio Pottery.

COLLECTORS' NOTES

For later artists, the problems of attribution are solved; most have their own mark or monogram, or an agreed motif which may be registered with the Craft Council in London.

During the earlier part of the Arts and Crafts movement, there were a great number of lesser-known potters working in the country, and these are still affordable. The work of the Martin brothers, William Moorcroft, and so on are now bringing prices in the hundreds and even thousands, but there are very attractive wares by Cadborough, Belle Vue and Minton Hollins that may be worth investing in their modest prices of £10-25. Most Ruskin pottery is climbing fast out of our limit, but you can still find marked miniatures at £45.

1. This teapot, Clarice Cliff's Crocus pattern of the 1930s, was priced at £75, way below its market value of £200 or more. She is being faked so often now that any Cliff piece must be suspect. Look for strong, easy brushwork lines, clear colours and good potting of the shape. Copies are a bad yellow and mushy-peas green.

Better to do some research and look for other designers and less-publicised names than buy what is already too expensive.

3.

4. Pilkington is known for commercial ceramics. It is certainly not known for its art pottery. And yet, from the early 1900s to 1938, when the studio was closed, the company made some very intriguing wares. Royal Lancastrian was their major tradename, and some are of considerable quality with flambé and other lustre glazes. Some prices are over our limit but this group from 1928-1930 are all under £100.

3. A collection of tiles made c.1910-1930. While older tiles and Art Nouveau patterns of Morris and de Morgan have reached the fashionable level, there are many beautiful and interesting tiles of a slightly later date which can build into a good collection. Look for unusual glazes and colours; many factories had small studios for experimental work. £12-20 each.

2. A funny little pot, with a squashed-in spout and a cut-out handle. Very Art Deco, made in Scotland at a small local pottery in the 1930s. The Cube Teapot Company of Leicester made an almost identical shape, and others copied this "revolutionary" idea (*Pottery Gazette*, 1925) but it's the gorgeous blue glaze that sets this off. More research! £25.

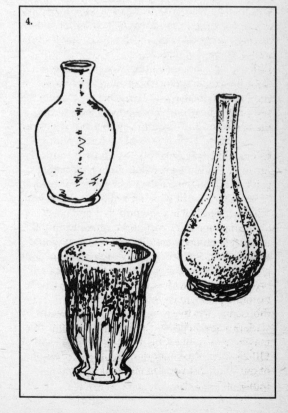

4.

Pottery

Pottery has long been the favoured material for the light-hearted. Inexpensive to make, available for experimentation by all sorts of semi-professional students and studio potters, it has somehow retained a kind of appropriate earthiness. Without the refinement of porcelain, our ceramic collections would be much the poorer, but without the energy and liveliness of pottery, our lives would be much less fun.

COLLECTORS' NOTES

The lack of obvious sophistication does not imply poor quality or workmanship. While much of the 18th and early 19th century pottery was fairly crude, that was more from the lack of experience in handling rather than the low standards of the makers. The wide marketing of production from the mid-19th century onwards meant that you can look for good wares, well potted, stable and well decorated and glazed.

Be wary of damaged pottery because once the glaze has been cracked it becomes very fragile and liable to flake off. Water gets taken up by the body underneath, which is porous, and so do stains. Restoration is quite possible, but it should be done as quickly as possible before staining occurs. Large areas of yellow or brown cannot be covered. And however skilful the restoration, you can no longer use the piece for hot or cold foods - more sensibly, not for food or water.

Because pottery is known to chip and crack easily, damage to the rim of a cup, for example, is acceptable on truly antique pieces which would be severely devalued if they were porcelain. Fine 17th and 18th century delftware or majolica will lose some value, but relatively little compared to the same on Sèvres or Meissen.

However, this laxity does not apply to most modern wares! Pottery of this century with chipped rims will be devalued in the sale room very considerably, so buy accordingly.

Most of all, enjoy what you buy, use it when you can and admire it when you can't.

1. The use of three-dimensional modelling goes back a long way, even before the work of Bernard Palissy in mediaeval France. But nothing really predicated the flood of relief patterns on tableware which came pouring out of the potteries from the 1930s right through until the 1950s.

Carlton Ware is one of the best known and most eagerly collected marks in this area. They particularly liked trees, tomatoes, cherries and berries on baskety backgrounds, like this cress dish and its stand, c.1938, £40

There are other names to look for: Shorter made cheese dishes and ribboned hats or bees perching on honeypots; Wade's jam pots are prized, a favourite model with blackberries is quite rare and sought after. Prices are very modest compared with the current favourite, Clarice Cliff. Cliff pieces include quite a few relief designs. These few others I have mentioned range from £35-85; Cliff pieces are now £250 and up.

2. This has to take some sort of prize; the hen salt and peppers sit in the middle of a plate of eggs, the whole in a bright green. No mark, but it could have come from any of the previously mentioned companies. A guaranteed smile for only £15, and probably from the 1950s rather than earlier, because of the harsh colouring. Research might help to trace the factory; the design has to be unique, for neither I nor any of my dealer friends has seen anything like it.

3. The Poole pottery was revitalised by the Stablers, who brought them a fresh look at modern design in the 1920s. These two matt-glazed candelabras are typical of their work in the 1930s, all in pastel colours. It was revived in the 1950s, so check the marks. C.1936, £50-60 each.

4. Chemists' jars were a mainstay of all commercial potteries until glass and then plastic wiped out the market. Now they are being reproduced for bathrooms and kitchens, especially in Italy and Portugal, and being sold in the most fashionable shops. Be very careful of reproductions; many are quite high quality with elaborate painting and designs. Look for signs of real use - slightly chipped edges, gathered dust or debris inside at the base, perhaps a nick or two out of the cover rim. The colours were strong and bold, usually white, dark blue or black. £55 at least for early 19th century originals.

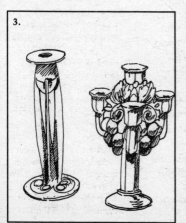

Prints and Etchings

Printmaking has sometimes been regarded, quite wrongly, only as a reproduction process, providing cheap decoration for the mass market. In fact, most of the photographic reproductions which are called prints by the general public are no more valuable than newspaper or magazine pictures, cut out and framed.

To the knowledgeable collector, prints refer to a very specific and demanding art form, which is created with ink and paper using one of three methods: from a raised surface, from an incised surface, or a flat surface. It's not a substitute for painting but a way of making multiple images, sometimes - as with dry-point - only a few, sometimes - as with woodcuts - many hundreds.

COLLECTORS' NOTES

Because so often the terms are confusing to the new collector, we've set out the various methods and techniques of printmaking, together with some hints as to how to recognise them and how the method might affect the value.

This section has a number of diagrams and details from various works, but there are an infinite number of artists who have worked during the time span which covers affordable work - roughly the 19th and 20th centuries.

But do remember that older prints need not necessarily be expensive. Many fine Japanese woodblocks can be bought for under £100, and even more astonishing, Renaissance prints - and even drawings - by famous artists turn up for much less because of their poor condition or fragmented state.

Although they may not be a particularly good long-term investment, they will teach you a great deal about the various methods and about paper quality. Many are available at such low cost because early print collectors and even museums did terrible damage to their prints by clipping the margins and mounting them on sheets of new paper for display. This can destroy almost all the sale room value, even of a Rembrandt.

1. Woodcuts and lino cuts, beloved of craft courses, are made in the same way; a drawing is made on the surface of a block of wood (or lino) and then everything on the surface around the lines is cut away.

Ink is applied with a roller, the surface is wiped clean, and then a paper is pressed on top, either by hand or in a press. The paper picks up the ink in the cut-away areas, leaving the wiped lines in white.

Look for good-quality paper, clean white lines with no smudging, and blacks which are really black and not speckled with white or pale marks, unless these are obviously deliberately part of the design.

Woodcutting is the oldest form of print-making and it also has had a great revival since the bold shapes and linear designs of the 1920s became popular.

This first detail is from a mediaeval woodcut. Late mediaeval woodcuts by unknown artists, in poor condition or with the repetitive images of saints or plants can be relatively inexpensive at only £80 or £90 because they were used to illustrate so many volumes of religious stories and herbals.

They can also be useful in developing a series of woodcuts in various national and cultural idioms.

Woodcuts

2. Modern artists have re-discovered the woodcut, and there are some truly lovely prints now coming up at auction and with those dealers who specialise in contemporary art. Galleries or individual dealers don't always include the earlier part of this century in their stock. Yet the 1920s in particular was a rich time for the manipulation of strong forms and linear patterns, perfectly suited to the medium. Persevere if you don't find a great deal immediately.

Look for good quality paper, with ample margins. Remember that narrow margins can affect the value badly.

Woodcuts should have clean lines with very bright white areas, and in contrast very dense black areas. Look for confident handling of strong subjects that suit the method.

Japanese colour prints are made in the same way except that there will be a separate woodblock prepared for each colour, and the print is taken down the line, each time pressed onto the block and lifted carefully.

With such multiple placings registration is vital; watch out for blurry edges or places where the colour prints over its containing line. This will be far less valuable.

This black and white print from the 1950s by J. Bostock, £40-50.

Prints and Etchings

The next form of printing to become established in Europe was engraving. Line engraving is an intaglio process, where the line which will print black is gouged out of the copper plate, using a fine v-shaped tool called a burin, to cut into the metal. Cross-hatching is used to achieve gradations of tone.

Woodcuts deal largely in blocks of shapes, while engraving is entirely linear. The fine channel that the burin cuts gives the engraving its light, calligraphic look; if you think of the appearance of copper-plate handwriting, you will have a good idea of what engraving at its best can do.

Our classical engravings are based on two traditions; an engraving "after" a painting, which is an attempt to produce a likeness of one art form in another, and the engravings which were developed through fine work on jewellery by goldsmiths. This was intrinsically lighter and more fluid, full of curves and curlicues.

During the 18th century, engravers gradually moved into working with aquatint and etching, so that pure line engraving was left more and more to reproduction.

COLLECTORS' NOTES

In an engraving, look for skill in drawing - the technique is quite difficult because of the resistance of the metal. Smooth curves are usually possible only by rotating the plate rather than the burin. If the artist cannot control the burin, then no amount of skill in printing will give life to the work.

In an etching, the artist has an easier time, but the technical knowledge used to control the acid bath becomes vital.

Look for differences in perspective and space; by using the stopping process a landscape can be peopled with figures that fade gently into the distance or become sharp and clearly seen in the foreground.

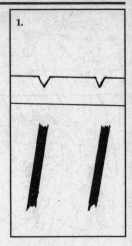

1. The top shows the cross-section view of the copper plate and the v-shape groove of the burin. Below that is the line the tool makes, as seen from above.

2. Detail from 19th century engraving. The complex line full of light and movement. By P. Dumont, c.1885, £40.

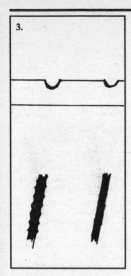

3. At the top, the diagram shows a cross-section of a copper plate after the acid has bitten into the plate.

The etching is made on a sheet of metal, which can be copper, zinc or steel. A film of wax is applied to the surface and the artist draws directly on the metal with a rounded scribe, removing only the wax, not digging into the metal at all. Below in the diagram is the slightly soft line which the scribe makes.

The plate is then dropped into a bath of acid which eats away the metal where the wax has been removed.

The plate is cleaned, and inked. Damp paper is laid over the plate and it goes into a press. This pushes the paper down into the etched lines, which picks up the ink.

Although it seems laborious in fact etching is much easier than engraving, as there is little resistance from the wax, and the artist can work quite spontaneously.

Rembrandt used to take wax plates with him when he went sketching and he drew directly onto the plate as if it were an ordinary pad of paper; when you remember that the artist must draw in reverse, it is remarkable.

4. Detail from a typical early 20th century engraving by Ribot, Paris.The portrait is simple and straightforward, with none of the studied formality so often seen in engravings. The ease of execution has given this a charm and directness almost akin to drawing. £40.

Another advantage the modern etcher has is the technique of stopping out; after the plate has been in the acid for a short time, it is removed and some chosen lines can be filled with wax or shellac before the plate is dipped in acid again. The result will give a very light etching of the wax-protected lines, while the second bath digs deep and creates richer textures. Look for the variety of depth of black which shows off this subtle art.

Prints and Etchings

Mezzotint, aquatint and dry-point are all variations on the theme of etching. The effects are subtly different and may not be too important to a new collector or the casual buyer of an attractive print for the hall. However, as experience and knowledge increase, it becomes more and more vital in assessing value and quality to be able to tell one from the other.

COLLECTORS' NOTES

Mezzotint, difficult to show in a diagram, is the result of attempting to reproduce the tones of an oil painting. The entire plate is roughened by a rocking tool, until, if printed, it would be entirely black. Areas are smoothed here and there where lines and tones are wanted.

The result is many more tones than usual in a black and white print; mezzotint was almost always used with early colour printing to imitate painting. Since the development of modern colour printing it is more or less obsolete.

Aquatint was invented by Leprince in France to create the same rough surface - this time by sprinkling resin on a metal plate before heating. The resin sticks as a dust, and under a magnifying glass you can see little white dots on a black background. Gradations of tones are not subtle - most aquatints use only a few. Goya was the greatest practitioner of them all.

Many modern artists use a version of the method called sugar aquatint, working on a layer of black gouache without engraving it first.

Dry-point uses a needle directly on bare metal. The line is thin and delicate with a light burr on either side as the tool just skims the surface. The burr adds richness by picking up additional ink, an effect which Rembrandt used constantly.

For the collector, dry-point has an added advantage; it can't be printed too many times as the burr wears down, so an edition is necessarily more limited than with an ordinary etching.

Many of the artists who did a lot of etching used methods in combination.

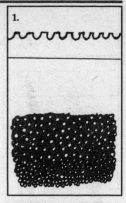

1. Top, cross-section of an aquatint plate ready for printing; below, the surface you would see with a magnifying glass. Carrying a glass with you all the time is one way to make sure you appreciate what you are buying.

2. A detail from an aquatint, showing that the dots can be graded to run from wide apart to close together. See the diagram above for an enlargement. This from a work by I. Martini, c.1948, £60.

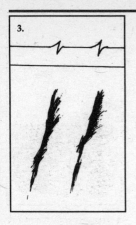

3. Top, cross-section of a dry-point plate with its characteristic ridges which will pick up more ink. Below, looking down at the distinctive dry-point line on a printed paper.

4. A dry-point etching, showing its light effect used to considerable advantage. Many artists use dry-point in combination with ordinary line engraving to contrast the heavier ink quality of the gouged-out metal and the thinner linear quality of dry-point. 1920, Joseph Hecht, £80.

5. Rembrandt etchings are not necessarily expensive. This fairly commonplace subject is one of the thousands which he made. Printed after his death and with its margins cut off by an earlier collector, its value is only £40-50, but as it uses both dry-point and line engraving, it's a learning tool, c.1656.

Prints and Etchings

Of all the techniques of printmaking, the most fruitful in commercial terms has been lithography. First invented by a Czech printing family in 1796, they had a soft, fine-grained stone as a bed for rolling ink while printing text in the normal way. Father and son found that drawing in chalks on the stone could be protected with gum and made permanent. The stone lasted longer than any previous base for printing.

Throughout the 19th and early 20th century it was used for almost all commercial printing in long print runs. Posters, postcards, inexpensive prints and all sorts of ephemera were turned out, sometimes hand tinted with watercolour, and now quite valuable.

Today, commercial printing has gone on to aluminium plates, and lithography is being used as an art form for the first time by printmakers who are interested in the special texture that stone brings to their work.

COLLECTORS' NOTES

Lithographs were run off in large quantities, so that the original printings were never considered particularly valuable. Hence its use in posters and postcards; it's their survival that has given them collectability.

For fine books, when good-quality colour printing was still in its infancy, illustrations were printed on the lithograph press in black and white and then individually hand coloured and tipped, or glued, into each copy. This was very common with botanical illustrations.

To identify a lithograph you must look at the lines under a magnifying glass; you'll see the soft, blurry edge, like no other medium, which the stone gives to the print. The major hazard for the collector is cheap screened prints, but look closely at one of the finer lines, perhaps some of the lettering under a magnifying glass; the dots of screened printing will be clearly visible. In a lithograph, you would see a granular texture from the stone, but not tiny, regular dots.

1. The lithographic line, above and below showing how the chalk or wax crayon can make many soft gradations, quite different from the sharper lines of an engraving or etching tool.

2. A lithograph of onions, showing the chalky texture which stone gives to even the simplest image. Artists of the 1930s and 1940s made many book illustrations and the results should be interesting to a collector. J. Scott, 1927, for a gardening magazine; £15.

3. A quickly sketched landscape in a 1939 French art magazine, *Verve*. Work produced on the stone could be drawn quickly and easily, the effect could be serious (or humorous) and instant and topical copy could be sketched and printed very quickly. It was, in short, the newspaper and magazine publishers' idea of heaven.

Original prints from 1890-1910 by well-known names can now be sold for thousands, but there is some good-quality work, from the pre-war period (*not* screen-printed reproduction) which is affordable and still worthwhile. This one by J. Kleister, c.1939, £50. Art magazines sometimes pasted in their lithographs without printing on the back; these are more valuable than text pages.

4. and 5. Posters have been a success story for some years now, and there are collectors who not only look for old ones, but go around taking the new issues off hoardings for future investment. The field is plagued by screen-printed reproductions sold for a few pounds, and sometimes expensively framed, making it difficult for a new collector to distinguish it from an original lithograph. Don't buy it unless you are sure you are not buying a modern colour print. These two are typical; on the left, a black and white poster from France, c.1900, not signed, and so a reasonable £90. On the right, a 1950s' English poster, £65.

Scent Bottles

The perfumes of Arabia do sweeten our lives, and there have been scent bottles of glass, ceramic and precious stones since the 13th century in Venice. Excavations in Egypt suggest that they go back much further to the trailed glass and hollowed stone cosmetic jars found in the royal tombs. Scent today comes in such magnificent commercial bottles that extra ones for the handbag are becoming rare and collectors of the future will suffer accordingly.

COLLECTORS' NOTES

Scent bottles fall into two categories; those that were made for personal use, and those usually called perfume bottles in this country, which are supplied by the manufacturers with their product. In the past, the personal ones were the most decorative. However, since the 1920s, top designers have been commissioned by the great couture and perfume houses of Paris to create containers for their products. Lalique, Baccarat and others began with spectacular bottles now high on the list of any collector, and their finest bottles can now bring not hundreds but many thousands of pounds.

The collector may well decide that buying perfume today should be influenced by the bottle as well as the contents for future investment.

The best small bottles have double tops; an inner dropper is closely stoppered, and then held tightly in place with the outer cap.

During the 19th century, many classical designs were revived and were made in the equivalent of costume jewellery - i.e., gilt metal, brass or such, set with glass stones and ovals of porcelain or pottery. Make sure that what you see is complete - you can easily miss a few empty settings or a cracked glass insert.

Condition is vital, not just because cracked or broken bottles can't be used, but because there are enough around to make poor examples a drag on the market, and very difficult to resell.

1. A Roman bottle, very small, which may have been used for oil, for scent or perhaps for poison.

Roman glass used to be inexpensive and plentiful in England; now whole examples are scarce, and Middle Eastern glass, chemically made iridescent to look like the original, is being sold as genuine. Even a tiny original like this will cost you near £100.

2. A ceramic scent bottle of the late 18th century, or rather its 19th century fake made in Paris by Samson. Now these bring a really good price, for their fine quality is far superior to much old pottery! Most were marked somewhere with a tiny "S", shown below the bottle in the drawing. £85.

3. Of the older kind of scent bottle within our range, the prettiest and most accessible are late Georgian. They are in plentiful supply, since almost every woman carried at least three or four with various kinds of scent and restorative liquids. They were made in clear, ruby or green glass, and many were double-ended, that is, two glass compartments in a slender shaft with a silver cap at either end.

One was usually a scent bottle, and the other a vinaigrette for fainting fits. That would have a perforated inner lid, while the scent bottle had a tiny glass stopper.

Most of these double bottles are now over our limit, but single ones are not. They were also made, like our pretty example above, in a slightly squarer shape for the dressing table. The silver cap could be very ornamental, and the glass is usually fluted or cut. Look for undamaged glass, and no dents in the silver. This one, 1831, £55.

4. The French turned out many variations for the handbag. This one , c. 1880, in 800 silver with a few enamelled leaves here and there. Very pretty and well made for what was essentially costume jewellery, it's only £35.

5. An impressive little bottle with a matching stopper - one of the points to look for. Unfortunately in this case the whole bottle, stopper and all, is a modern moulded cheap one, with a thin layer of flashed iridescent glass. But at £8, it's hardly fake!

6. Another French production, with panels of porcelain set in gilt metal. Probably 1920s or later, unmarked, but quite pretty with matching engraving on the little top. £15, of no lasting value but fun to have on the shelf.

7. I bought this for a few pounds at a car boot sale, and unhappily sold it before I had time to do a little research. It was matt black glass, with a glossy tulip in relief on the front. I'm sure it was made for a very classy 1930s' scent; keep boxes or labels you buy with any perfume - help the collector to do the necessary research! As it was, unmarked and unknown, £18.

Sewing Collectables

One of my pleasantest discoveries was a jar of brass thimbles brought by a friend to the market. It had come from a one-room Norfolk school at the turn of the century when every child learned how to sew as a matter of course. They were all sizes from the tiniest for a child of four or five to an almost-adult size, and we sold them reluctantly one by one, happily to many mothers with young children. Most collectors of sewing things are women and many embroider or do other kinds of needlework. There is an atmosphere about these needlework tools that brings an instant whiff of lavender bags and workboxes full of quilts. One good thing is that the prices range from literally a few pence for a box of Edwardian pins to many hundreds for a fine inlaid sewing box with ivory fittings. Everyone can be a collector with that choice ahead!

COLLECTORS' NOTES

You have to be an assiduous searcher to collect in this very domestic subject; so much was made up of little trinkets and gadgets, bought for very little and seldom valued except as convenient utensils. Keep an eye out for unusual things.

Sewing needles were stored in carved ivory bodkins, but also in faded velvet scrapbooks and, with embroiderers, on pieces of canvas.

Crochet hooks and knitting needles were often kept in home-made cases with pockets for each size. They can be botched rags or works of art.

Don't forget about sewing baskets, boxes and work-tables. Every household had its special place where needles and threads were kept. Ask in your family, too, as well as looking at house clearance sales.

Many boxes and baskets sold from the home are still full of the owner's bits and pieces. You may find, as I did recently, hand-made strips of lace, a few jet buttons, a needlecase in 1920s' leather, and best of all, a pile of materials kept for quilt-making.

1. Chinese carving was much in demand for lacquer sewing boxes and hundreds of tiny sewing accessories like this needle case. Many of the boxes came completely fitted; this is likely to have been in one, but it's all that has survived. Watch out for broken carvings or cracks in the ivory which would halve its modest value of £18-25. A box with all its fittings would be well into the top hundreds because they are now so rare.

2. A few jet buttons, £2 each. Useful for jewellery and such. Check that they aren't glass (see p.78).

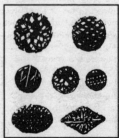

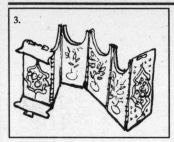

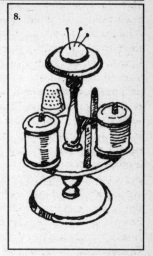

3. A tiny needle case of thin sheet brass pressed into the shape of a Japanese screen. Each fold is doubled so that the needles slide inside, and the whole clips together with a tiny hook. Numbers on each fold correspond to needles sizes, from five to nine. The brass is imprinted stating that this is the English Woman's Needle Case of New Design, 1904. £12.

7. A silver hallmarked thimble in its case, 1916, embossed with pretty flowers in silver gilt and initialled "from A to R". Thimbles have become a source of collector's folly - there is no other word for it. Porcelain ones in particular are decorated with crests of cities, with coats of arms or with little mottoes. Almost all are new but genuinely old ones, £35.

8. The aristocrat of the sewing room was a dolly for spools of thread. Many were made in fine woods with carved ivory spindles, others are simple pine constructions probably made at home from bits and pieces in the workshop. This is very much at the covetable end; although quite small the wood is ebony and cherry, with boxwood lines in green. The top pincushion is in beaded tapestry embroidery, something I've only seen once before. C.1870, £85-95 for similar models; check for broken spindles.

4., 5. and **6.** The most important factors for the collector of pincushions are unusual materials or images, and the condition of the cushion itself. With rare exceptions damage is confined to the edges of the object, but look carefully anyway. I've seen one silver pin cushion shaped like a Venetian gondola where the top of the prow had broken off, and the estimate was halved at once. Original cushions are well tucked in, with only very narrow folds and usually quite pin-pricked and faded. Replacements are usually thicker, of velvet rather than Victorian plush, too bright, and seldom have any holes. These three are all genuinely pinned; the silver hedgehog hallmarked 1912, £35, the moccasin beaded and probably c.1920, £18, and the wooden painted Dutch souvenir shoe dated 1902, £12.

Shelves

No collector ever turns down a chance to acquire a pleasant set of shelves. Once you begin collecting you will need somewhere to put them, and it might as well be shelves which suit your own collection as well as your room.

COLLECTORS' NOTES

Let the display fit the contents. If you collect porcelain boxes of elegant refinement, they won't look particularly well on shelves of rough country pine. Obviously there are some styles which can be adapted to anything, so these are always at a premium; simple mahogany without too much inlay or fuss, well-polished pine with a little extra style.

Watch out for damage to the struts. Wall shelves are especially liable to break off where they are pierced with holes and it is difficult to mend the set without a very clumsy extra batten.

Many sets of shelves in the 1920s and 1930s now look quite pleasantly aged, but they were made, especially in the 1930s, with poor wood of appalling quality. It may not be apparent until they simply fall apart. Test shelves gently by leaning on the individual shelf, to see if it bends.

Look for dresser tops if you have plates. The groove at the front of each shelf is a wonderful way of preventing accidents. But don't be tempted to rely on that alone.

Style is always a good indication of value. While most shelves you find will be in classic styles - basic scrolled or straight sides - there are always a few with definite influences from Art Nouveau and Art Deco. When these are interpreted well, they make stunning additions to your room and perhaps to your collection. Look for pewter hinges on cupboards and interesting panels of stained glass, not the rippled glass of cheap copies.

While most shelves are wood, by being away from the floor they suffer less from woodworm than other pieces of furniture. However, they can be infested - look hard for those tell-tale holes.

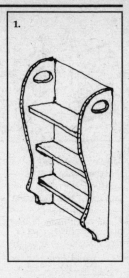

1.

1. Shelves which fit in small spaces and yet don't look too twee are very useful. This set of pine shelves was particularly attractive because there was a thin bead of brass running down the front of each side piece.

Look carefully to make sure that the beading is continuous. If it is broken, you'll have to replace the whole piece and narrow beading like this is not easily available.

Remember, too, that you should think about lacquering the brass, or you will continually be polishing the edges of the shelves as they will grow black with the residue.

When I see small shelves like these, I buy them without measuring first - I'll find a place. 1910s, £45.

2. A more traditional set of shelves, often in oak or mahogany rather than pine. The battens at the back where the shelves are hung on the wall may be quite fragile. Often they were added later, as the set was originally made to sit on top of a side table.

Openwork sides look very pretty but are even more liable to crack. Watch out for shapes that have been enlarged to hide broken bits; they are hard to see sometimes. C.1865, oak, £75.

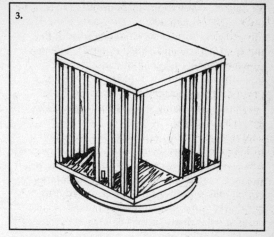

3. A classic style, dating from Victorian times but made right up to the war, and revived recently. It was usually made in solid hardwood, sometimes in black lacquer with painted decoration. Make sure the revolving top swings around without creaking. Probably not for your collection, but for your reference books. 1920s, polished rosewood with a good finish, £95.

5. A tall, thin bookcase with a cupboard closed in stained glass. Art Deco influence, nice blondish oak with pewter hinges making it desirable. These depend entirely on the quality of the wood and skilfulness in using the design. Bad ones are hideously clumsy. But this pleasant shape, 1938, £70.

4. Adapted from a mantelpiece, this set of pine shelves was painted when it first adorned a country room. Now we usually strip them, which can loosen the joints. Watch out for breaks along the back; when these were wrenched out of the wall, many broke and were badly repaired. Support them with an extra batten. C.1900, carved pine and beech, £95.

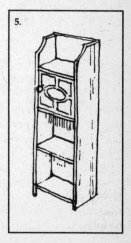

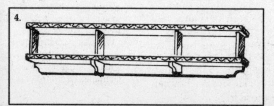

Silver

Silver has been mined for thousands of years, yet most of the silver used in Europe from the 15th to the 19th centuries came from one source, the mines of Central and South America. The metal was almost a by-product of the search for gold - the mythical kingdom of Eldorado - but it proved riches enough, plundered by the Spaniards and brought home in the great ships of the treasure fleet.

Silver was, and is, prized for its lustre and utility, and the ease with which it can be worked into an endless succession of decorative styles. It is also safeguarded by a system of hallmarks which makes dating a matter of record. But hallmarks can and are faked or moved, so in spite of what many buyers believe, they cannot always be relied on.

Although larger and more important pieces are beyond the price range of this book, there are a surprising number of sterling and silver-plate objects which are available. And practical silver is used to make the tableware we can enjoy every day; see p. 62 and p.170 as well for a look at cutlery of all kinds. But first, the material itself.

COLLECTORS' NOTES

"Sterling" silver is simply a way of describing how much pure silver is included in the alloy. Almost no 100% silver is made - it is too soft and would distort too easily in your hand.

The recognised standard in Great Britain and the United States is 924 parts silver to 1,000 parts of finished metal. Every piece of silver made or imported for sale into this country is marked appropriately by the assay offices.

There is a slightly higher grade, marked by the addition of the "Britannia" punch, of 958 pure silver. This was obligatory between 1697 and 1720 and had its own mark, but today it is optional only. Not to be confused with Britannia metal, a soft pewter made in the 19th century with 98% tin, often electro-plated with silver and marked EPBM.

1. Trinkets for the table include little pieces like this menu card holder. The shape of the bird is split and the card would be inserted between its wings; marked 1875, Birmingham, and once probably sold in a set of six or twelve.

Card holders make an interesting collection - I have seen them in the shapes of flowers, wreaths and one particularly colourful American Christmas wreath set enamelled in green white and red.

Art Deco styles are very collectable - look for squares or circles with black enamel sections.

Boxed sets would be quite valuable as they are seldom found. Like all Victorian silver, they were mass-produced for the middle-class dining room, so you might collect a set of matching pieces or a harlequin set of different ones on the same theme. This single one, the light wings in good condition and hallmarked, £40.

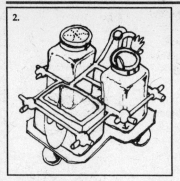

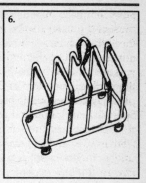

2. This square, simple cruet is marked 1925, Birmingham, where many of the tablewares were made.

The uncut glass bottles and salt dish have two circles of engraving on the caps. The round ball-ended rails are similar to designs by Christopher Dresser. This exact model was also made in plate. £65.

3. A larger and more expensive cruet with cut glass bottles. Make sure they all match and fit their spaces well. Silver plate, £65.

4. and **5.** Napkin rings are another collectable of almost limitless decoration. Many people concentrate on frilly edges, on animal engraving or repoussé work. From about £20-40 each.

6. A tiny toast rack, too small to hold anything except slivers of slimming bread. But perfect for letters. This was one of a pair, so although simple and light, they were £95; hallmarked 1916.

7. A wonderful Victorian breakfast dish holding toast, butter or jam, a knife, and a bell to ring for the maid when you were ready for coffee. Hallmarked 1882, Birmingham again, and a design that continued to be made for another ten or twenty years.

Make sure the glass dish and spoon sit in their holders and match the design; many are replacements. £98. Other toast racks were made in all sizes from the tiny one shown above to quite substantial family pieces, but this combination is unusual. Look for other multi-function pieces.

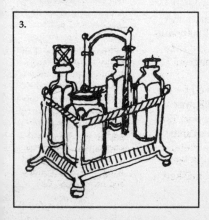

Silver

Most continental countries have a second grade of sterling at 800 or 840 parts per 1,000 for cheaper production, or for those objects which need the extra strength of added base metal. This is usually marked with an appropriate punch or simply with the number 8, 80 or 84.

Plating methods: Silver plate is a thin layer of pure silver on a base metal. Estimating the value of plate becomes quite difficult in practice, since there is no equivalent standard for quality, nor any obvious way of knowing what is the base metal without scratching, a practice frowned upon by eagle-eyed stall holders.

Sheffield 18th century platemakers used ingots of silver on copper sheet, working and decorating the object in the same way as sterling, although the pieces are unmarked except for the maker. This practice gradually died out when electro-plating came in around 1840-1880. Old Sheffield plate, with its lovely warm colouring reflected from the copper base, has a cachet and a rarity value of its own and can be as expensive as sterling, unless the silver is very worn and the copper shows through in too many places.

Electro-plating involved making a piece in base metal, usually nickel silver, and then lowering it into a bath where pure silver is deposited as a thin coating. The finish is a brighter and a colder colour than Sheffield; it is usually marked EPNS (electro-pated nickel silver). It can be replated quite easily, which has lead to the practice amongst dealers nowadays to do that. The result is an over-bright colour, and an absence of the pleasant, mellow light-and-dark effect a good patina brings.

For collectors, replating is generally a bad thing, unless you're prepared to wait fifty years or so for a patina to develop again. Decorators like the bright colour - it certainly shines on the table - but avoid it when you can.

Until recently, Britannia replating was hard to do and repairs are still difficult, so that damaged or worn pieces lose a lot of their value.

1.

1. A magnificent centrepiece for any table; this standing fruit dish, sometimes called a tazza, is a cut crystal bowl sitting on a stand of writhing silver shapes. The form is based on a vine with bunches of grapes dripping from all sides, the whole wrapped around with bark-like textures and even a little bird's nest.

If this were in sterling silver, it would be late Victorian naturalism at its most expensive, but in plate it becomes a very reasonable £65, adding another £50 premium on top of the doubled price for a pair.

One of the great advantages with plate, which is otherwise undated, is that many designs were offered in either silver or plate, so that if we can date the sterling, we can date our plate copy. This one is likely to be c.1880.

2. A unique coffee set, almost certainly made at Keswick or one of the other Institutes which encouraged amateur artists and craftspeople to try their hand at making their own goods. This hand-made tea set doesn't quite work - some of the joins have opened because of lack of experience in handling the metal. But the silver is on copper, a good heavy plate, the design is the best of Arts and Crafts, and the whole so handsome that I hated selling it. £99, unmarked.

4. The graceful shape of a coffee pot in perfect condition. The cane handle is pristine, the whole effect brilliant. C.1930, plate, absolutely lovely and a steal at £55. In sterling silver at least £170, I think.

3. A sweet or bon-bon dish in baroque style, but made c.1914. The openwork is attractive but a bit heavy handed, and the cartouche for the monogram is bare, a good asset for a new buyer. £60.

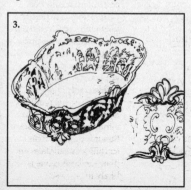

Silver

One of the great assets for collectors is the number of objects that were made of silver, or with silver. The range is enormous, and so the chances of finding good things at almost any market or sale are increased. Silver is so durable and practical as well as beautiful that you are sure to find things which will give you pleasure in using them every single day, as well as for display.

COLLECTORS' NOTES
Learn to know the makers' marks as well as the hallmarks. Hallmark books are made so conveniently small that you can carry one with you all the time, but there are fewer books that give you information about makers. Yet many a fake has been spotted because the hallmarks may have looked good, but the maker's mark was inappropriate for the period or the style.

Another reason for learning about the silversmiths and manufacturers was shown up recently by the research of a leading magazine. They took an otherwise basic late 18th century silver salver to a number of dealers, including a well-known auction house. Everyone, including the specialist dealer, took one look and made a hurried judgement that undervalued the salver by at least 100% simply because the rare maker's mark wasn't recognised. Foreign marks are another area much neglected by the Anglo-Saxon public, including our American visitors. Learn to recognise Russian, French and other Continental marks and you may find more hidden treasure.

Such diligence and homework is also valuable for the budget buyer, in that silver of this century is still under-valued, and the names of even the most respected designers and silversmiths are largely unrecognised by the general public. It's a rare chance to find really good pieces at reasonable prices.

One advantage of buying at the bargain level is that fakery is less likely - there's not enough return for the deception to be profitable.

1. A drinking cup which holds a glass for hot tea, or toddies. The design is elaborate repoussé, with scenes of cupids and nymphs, flowers and foliage, all impossible to clean easily, and needing an enormous amount of elbow grease to keep polished.

Marked 80, and probably German or Austrian, c.1875, and individually about £75. I have seen a similar cup in plate of some kind selling for only £15 and an entire set of twelve at £500, with their glasses intact.

The lower grades of sterling are not highly regarded in England, and resale may be difficult.

Collectors take perhaps too much comfort from the assurance of English or American markings, and under-value the lesser grades of silver considerably. I've had dealers turn away from delightful little novelties at very reasonable prices because they felt their own buyers would be wary. You must decide for yourself.

2.

3.

2. A tiny candelabra, perhaps even a miniature for a doll's house. The style is of the 1880s, the engraving is very delicate and must have taken someone hours and hours for each little branch.

Miniature wax candles are put into the sconces, although one is missing.

What appears to be doll's house furniture of silver is usually for display on side tables in little groups, rather than for children to play with. 1918, £55.

Look for marks - they are sometimes omitted because the pieces were so small and there are no miniature marks in use. Then only the sterling lion might be used.

3. Many houses in the country still used candles to light their way to bed even after gas lighting was available.

Chambersticks are the name given to these; they have a larger dish underneath for ease of carrying and to avoid dripping wax on the hand.

The lovely Art Nouveau decoration makes this expensive. Look for repairs on the handle which is the weakest part and often broke off in use. C.1910, £95.

5. A silver belt, mounted on navy grosgrain. These are not just for nurses, as many think, but were fashionable with the droopy chiffons of the 1910s. Only one side is hallmarked, so make sure the fabric is sturdy enough to keep the belt safe. 1912, Birmingham, £55.

4.

4. Card cases were an important accessory before the Filofax came into use. They are larger and flatter than compacts of a similar date. This is of tortoiseshell with silver mounts and a silver Maltese cross in the centre.

Make sure the hinge is working - they can be very awkward to repair. Check the edges, too, where the shell could chip. £65.

5.

Silver

Silver and ceramic fashions in tableware often go hand in hand; many of us think that both are essential to the setting out of a good meal. But novelties also have their fashion and during the 19th century the heavy hand of Victorian respectability was lightened a little by their enjoyment of toys and trinkets. Even to the most modest collector, these are affordable and are as varied in style and subject as anyone could wish.

COLLECTORS' NOTES

It always makes sense to buy the best you can afford, but with these silver trinkets it's particularly helpful to buy silver and not silver plate. Most silver novelties were made or finished by hand, as they are today; the work involved is high compared to the relatively low value of the metal.

Victorian trinkets, mostly dating from the second half of the 19th century, were full of animals. There are chicken coop carts, monkey inkwells and lots of cats, especially used as handles on cream pots.

With the changing fashions and the opening up of the Japanese Empire in the late 1860s, the craze for oriental design shows in little vases traced with peach blossoms, kimono-clad ladies holding up knife rests and, since Chinese and Japanese seemed equally exotic to the customers, coolie-hatted salts and peppers.

Be careful of certain patterns which have been used by reproduction houses - especially young ladies' heads or cupids in a group of three or four. These appear on mirror backs, on little boxes and bottles, on anything and everything. The lesson is the same for every other kind of antique - if you see it too often, it's likely to be a copy. (A copy, not a fake, for they are usually and genuinely marked for their recent production year.) Even if you can't remember all the past hallmarks it's a good habit to learn the current alphabet, so you can recognise new work easily without wasting time.

1. Vesta cases were a product of the invention of safety matches which had to be carried separately with the striker on the outside. They date from c.1840 to c.1920. Most were of silver, metal, brass, or occasionally of wood. They form an ideal subject for a small collection because of their variety and range and, of course, the relatively low price.

This particular example is enamelled with the flag of a sailing club. Others come in the shape of books, or with sporting illustrations, with mother of pearl mounted in silver, made of agates or in ceramics and even in leather to look like a miniature camera. Prices according to the materials and the uniqueness of the decoration, but they start around £15, in silver from £25-50. This, 1928, £35.

Make sure they aren't badly dented or too damaged to open; like other pocket accessories, they were liable to get knocked around.

When lighters came into use, Vesta cases gradually disappeared.

2. Typical of the novelties in the early 1900s, this little Dutch pony cart may have had a pony as well, now lost. It was marked as an import for 1904. The sides of the cart are nicely engraved in woodgrain, with even the nails showing where the cart would have been hammered together. £55.

4. Knife rests were very useful, keeping the dirty utensil off the white table cloth during the meal. They are also made in a wide range of novelty designs; these crossed ends are common but the mother of pearl centres are very pretty. £40 for a pair. I have also bought a much more elaborate pair with rampant lions holding a twisted barred gate; these were more at £50 each.

3. A little rowing boat charm. Although most silver charms were mass-produced, this one is beautifully made by hand, with tiny oars that lock into place or can be removed, and even a bit of enamelled blue water washing around underneath the seats. A delight worth the extra cost of £38 compared to the usual £15-20. Marked Sterling, so probably Danish or American.

5. The worst buy of my life. Cranberry glass, cracked under the silver rim; worn plated top with bashed-open motifs for some impatient diner. Can't give it away.

6. Grape scissors somehow symbolise the luxury lifestyle. Maybe it's Mae West and "peel me a grape", but none of the other little Victorian and traditional table utensils sound so unredeemably posh. And yet they are very useful, quite different from other tableware and again come in a variety of appropriate designs and patterns. They seldom match the actual cutlery, but they did come with a nutcracker and nutpicks; a dessert implement set.

Look for unusual designs; I saw one with a hunting scene. The scissors can be sharpened. Sheffield, 1924, £65.

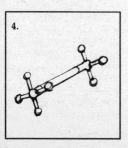

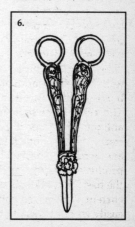

Souvenirs

"What's good about goodbye?" would have been written as an anthem for the tourist trade in souvenirs. Nor is it anything new - since before Alexander the Great sent back a piece of local pottery to his mother, the souvenir industry has been thriving and profitable wherever in the world people travel.

The first separation for the collector is an artificial one between souvenirs and commemorative pieces. Although souvenirs are not necessarily commemorative, all commemoratives are souvenirs, albeit of an event rather than a place. We have included both in this section to give you an idea of what is available, but there is such a wide variety of object, design and potential subject that, more than most, these are truly the tiniest sampling of what's there.

Early souvenirs, like Alexander's, are not likely to be marketed or named as such, although artists often included the name of their home town in their signature. It was the middle-class Victorians who wanted everyone to know that they had been on a holiday, and that your mug was a present from Redcar, or their own breakfast cups were a reminder of happy days at Bath. Others loved being able to visit an important event like the 1851 Exhibition and reminded themselves and their friends with something to prove it.

COLLECTORS' NOTES

Souvenirs vary in quality enormously from the really crude to almost works of art. Make a decision as to whether you are interested in all souvenirs, and then even seaside postcards are grist to your mill, or only in the best of mementos, with the added charm of nostalgia.

Many people concentrate on a particular place or a special event, like a coronation. Whatever your decision, look for as little damage as possible, although perhaps alone among the things in this book, the message on it is more important than the medium it comes attached to.

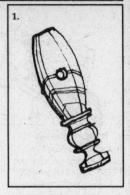

1.Victorians loved optical and mechanical souvenirs and this miniature agate telescope has six views of Edinburgh, which you can see through a microscopic lens. From one to twelve different pictures could be included.

Stanhopes were named after the Earl of Stanhope, although they were invented in 1853 by David Brewster, and continued to be made until the 1920s. Victorian ones are in most demand, or those with maps instead of views, nudes and hand-coloured views of anywhere. Pencils are very common and among the least expensive. Most Stanhopes are less than 6 or 7 cm long.

Unusual ones are getting hard to find. Look for them in gold and silver charms, vesta cases, sewing and needle cases, gold cufflinks, silver pens and pencils, bottle tops - almost anything.

Prices vary according to the scarcity of the object; this one £45, others £25-65.

2.

2. The Scottish traditions have left behind a legacy of wonderful souvenirs, eagerly sought by tourists and travellers to that magic country. This dram glass, c.1930 of heavily cut crystal with "Afor Ye Go" engraved on one side, represents one of the most appropriate, its thick bottom ensuring that the parting dram was only a short one! £12.

Other Scottish souvenirs were equally popular; almost anything in tartan, from the time that Queen Victoria redecorated Balmoral, was eagerly brought home, including tartan darning mushrooms, card cases, napkin rings, etc. Early examples of tartan souvenirs range from £25-55. A young girl's dress in tartan silk from the 1860s brought over £200 last year.

Mauchline ware, with its black printed landscapes on pale wood, is another favourite of Scottish collectors. Made in Ayr from the 1860s to c.1933 it brings from £25-90.

3. A pottery milk jug from Limerick with a black transfer print of an Irish wedding on one side, "Regards from Limerick" on the other. The body is rather creamy in colour and there's no other mark. Probably late 19th century and perhaps from a local pottery - imports from the Continent were usually white porcelain. £25.

4. Varicoloured sands are a feature of a few places in the Britain, and the Isle of Wight is one of the best endowed. Their use to fill clear bottles or other miniatures has been a tourist industry for centuries. Elaborate ones created landscapes or even complex pictures inside frames; they would be quite a lot more expensive. The simplest, like this c.1910 bottle, layered the colours like a dessert or ice cream, £22.

Today the souvenir shop sells empty bottles and offers a kind of pick and mix spread of boxes of sand , to make your own antique of tomorrow.

5. Souvenirs from abroad were always a popular buy, particularly when they had a motto one could quote knowledgeably to one's friends at home. This snail wins on all counts; French, escargot and l'amour! 1920s from Annecy, of white porcelain with flowered decoration. £18.

3.

4.

5.

Spoons

Collecting spoons is a delightful occupation. Thanks in part to the Victorians, whose idea of what an average household would require included the provision of twelve different kinds of spoon, there is an abundant choice. Add to that the numbers of individual silver tableware patterns, the odd kinds of spoons from horn to lacquer, and you have the richness of a kingdom to hand.

Then there are the display spoons or token spoons - not for use, but to serve a ritual purpose. Welsh love spoons come into this category, glass spoons from Venice, and others of similar intent.

COLLECTORS' NOTES

With rare exceptions, spoons are not individually expensive; if you are buying silver, it makes sense to buy sterling silver rather than plate unless you are collecting a set or you find a pattern with a particularly relevant or interesting theme. Or you might see an unusual kind of spoon which will give you an idea of what to look for in a better material - soda and ice cream spoons, for example are worth buying as plate because they turn up so seldom in sterling.

Not everything is silver, of course. Wooden spoons have a long history and some, particularly small boxwood spoons for mustard or general use are delightful enough to fit into anyone's display. Carved ceremonial spoons from Africa and India are intriguing as well as attractive. Look for accompanying boxes or papers as often as you can for added interest.

Although spoons were included in sets of cutlery, tea and coffee spoons were boxed in fours, sixes, eights and twelve and also sold separately. There are souvenir spoons with an amazing variety of shields, motifs, and symbols.

The join between the bowl and the handle is the weakest part. Any repairs will lower the value considerably. Be wary of plain spoons with fancy decoration added later to the bowl; simple handles almost always meant a simple bowl.

1. A cake spoon of elaborate style, hallmarked 1878. This broad-based server was perfect for small cakes and little pastries. It could also be used for serving anything relatively small, like individual portions of meat or desserts.

Both the handle and the flat serving plate are heavily engraved in a floriate pattern. It was dirty but perfect; watch out for lop-sided handles when they are as thin as this. Birmingham, £65.

1.

2. A delicate sugar sifter, the twisted rope turning into a comfortable handle. Watch out for kinks in the very thin handle. It might only look bent, but should you try to straighten it gently, you may find yourself with two pieces. Although repairs look easy, in fact with such thin and delicate designs it is almost impossible to make invisible repairs. Chester, 1910, £40.

3. We seldom see American silverware, except for small pieces like this really delightful Art Nouveau ice cream spoon, c.1900, with twining foliage stem, flower top, and narrow gilt bowl. Worth research - it has its manufacturer's stamp and "sterling" mark expected. C.1900, £16-18.

4. A Chinese spoon, in 80 silver, its handle decorated with wishes for a good life.

One of set of six spoons, and two large serving spoons, c.1920, £25.

Such trinkets from the Far East used to be ignored by British and Continental dealers, but recently they have begun to recognise their artistic as well as metal value.

A recent buy included some Indian napkin rings made in a very delicate pattern of tiny coins, with a matching little tray and five spoons. No doubt the remains of a complete tableware set made sometime around 1910.

Although a few years ago no local dealer would have looked at them in fact I sold both the Indian set and these Chinese spoons within a week.

5. Enamel spoons were imported from Norway in the 1900s; this set was beautifully engraved in silver-gilt and then coated over the back and handle in translucent white enamel. But once the enamel chip the value plummets.

Watch out for acrylic used as a repair; enamel cannot be fixed. This set, four in the original box marked with the royal coat of arms of Norway, and from a leading jeweller in the 1910s, £95. Norwegian display spoons , made around the same time and imported especially by Liberty's, can now bring hundreds of pounds.

6. Mote or strainer spoon, late 17th century, used to keep tea leaves out of cup. Silver, c.1795, £40.

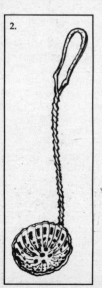

2.   3.   4.   5.   6.

Tables

Street markets and antique fairs are not the best place to find tables; a question of space, as with all furniture categories, comes into play. But there are plenty of affordable tables tucked away in second-hand shops, local auctions and even at those self-same markets and fairs, albeit often holding up the dealer's display. At least six times a year I sell a small side table or an even smaller stool off the stand, so if you see something tucked away under a lace tablecloth, ask.

COLLECTORS' NOTES

There are relatively few antique dining tables under £100, except for country pine. Most of the tables shown here are for occasional use in the home, although one or two can be utilised for light meals. If you do intend or need to put your table to use in that way, then nothing can replace the first prerequisite of stability.

Pine kitchen tables are still available in all sorts of variations; some were intended for dining tables and may have extra leaves. These bring a premium; they were more carefully made and often polished or at least waxed regularly. Look for the patina - it has a soft amber colour quite unlike the brash shade of modern varnish. Modern reproductions are also made from old wood; they can be very deceptive.

For smaller tables, pine was usually painted or lacquered; usually this has faded or rubbed off. Watch out for fake wear - it will be rubbed evenly all over the piece, including the underside which would normally never be touched.

Many collectors, particularly of kitchenalia, buy things that didn't start out as tables for occasional use; small stools, upturned pine churns, pine dough boxes and spinning mules have all been put to good use.

Indian pine, from a different species, is turning up more and more as boxes and small tables, much of it heavily carved and painted. Since even the new ones are often hand-made, it can be difficult to make any honest assessment of age.

1. Pine in disguise. This black painted table was meant to look like expensive oriental lacquer; the usual painted top was simulated by a stamped piece of silver metal in the centre of the top. But the legs are graceful and the small size makes it an extremely useful surface for a glass of wine, as long as you protect the rather fragile finish with a coaster.

However, the most interesting part of the table doesn't show in the drawing; it is completely dismountable, coming apart almost too easily for comfort into four legs, a top and a shelf.

Possibly made in the East for use in travelling homes and encampments, it cannot be permanently fixed without destroying the pretty and open appearance, so avoid putting anything hot or fragile on top. While the principle is quite common, this is the prettiest one I have seen so it earned its price of £40 quite easily; c.1910.

2. Pine as it is; nothing painted or decorated about this pembroke table, except that it probably started life in a country sitting room and only moved to the kitchen during this generation when anything of pine conjures up shades of Mrs Beeton.

The handles are original, with rather nice pine nuts on the inside into which the wooden handle screws tight. Watch out for pretentious refurbishing with drop handles in brass.

Check that the drawer runs easily; if the piece was originally painted or grained and then stripped commercially, the joints get very wet, the wood swells and the grain opens up, creating gaps between the slats and making drawers stick. Impossible to date accurately; c.1880-1920, £90 in reasonable condition with a decent colour. If a really good patina, add £25.

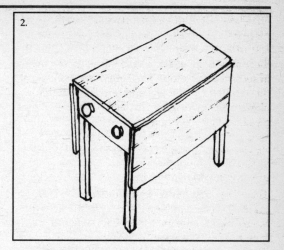

3. A pretty washstand with tiled back. No, not an original, but a 1950s' marriage between a single bed-head, some modern tiles and a quite ordinary side table. The two woods show sharply different colours where they meet. It fooled me in a dark store. Still, £45.

4. A French dough bin, or flour table; the shape suits the Lorraine region where it was found. Very heavy and a beautiful golden colour. Flour was safe inside during baking weeks. Huge dowelled legs to hold up the massive body with lift-up top. C.1900, £95-98.

Tables

Watch out for marriages, very common in tables and often made quite genuinely by the owners for their own use. New legs are put underneath old tops and old legs get a brand-new slab of wood on top. Sometimes the new wood is stained to try and match the original, but it seldom fools you once you start looking.

The only exception is a painted table, where the colour hides a lot. Country-made tables were, like country chairs, sometimes made out of a bit of this and a bit of that.

Make sure that all the legs are the same height. If it tilts, it may be the shop floor, or it may be a bit taken off one leg because of woodworm or a broken caster. Inexpensive tables were not necessarily treated with respect.

Tilt-top tables were a favourite English gimmick for making more space in crowded rooms, perfect for today's houses. But be warned; they are usually on tripod feet, and the feet come out too far for the table to stand against the wall.

Sometimes they are quite small - I've sold a tilt-top only a metre in diameter. Make sure the pivot is in working order; it was considered acceptable at one time to wedge them brutally to keep the top straight, and the wood can have cracked.

Look particularly carefully at the joints between the leg and the top; a stretcher or an apron underneath will help to keep the legs firm and straight. The apron is a wide piece of wood, sometimes up to 6 or 7 inches deep, forming the frame on which some table tops sit. French styles often have a deep apron, perhaps scrolled as well, and country kitchen tables often have a deep apron with a drawer or two.

One word of warning; our ancestors were generally shorter than we are. The apron can be too deep for tall men to sit comfortably. Measure up to the apron, not just the top height when you are deciding whether to buy; You can raise a table by adding casters to the feet, but that may damage them, or the ornamentation may make it impossible.

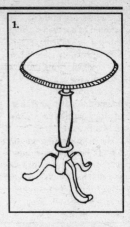

1.

1. A little tripod of rosewood, its top nicely edged with an arcaded border, the feet simple but sturdy. During the Victorian period, the dark red of rosewood appealed greatly to their predilection for rich colours. In the fancier pieces it was inlaid with brass or sometimes, to make it even darker, with black ebony lines. The most successful designs let the beauty of the grain show through without much exterior ornamentation.

Small tripods are sometimes called wine tables, carried from room to room, and set beside the host to hold a bucket or a wine tray. In fact they were used everywhere, holding little knick-knacks, tea, sandwiches, cakes, sewing baskets, or whatever. Make sure it is heavy enough not to be easily knocked over. In good condition, £65.

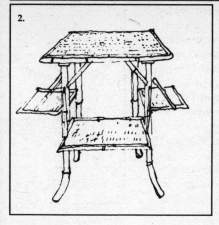

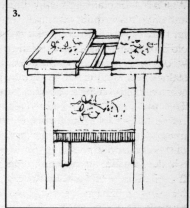

2. Bamboo was much beloved of the English family, in fakery, with chairs and tables painted to resemble bamboo and lacquer.

Here we have the real thing, a little what-not table for displaying pretty things. The splayed legs make it quite steady for such a light material - an important point when you are buying. The little side shelves come down in a curiously primitive but perfectly effective system of iron struts that slide in and up inside the hollow bamboo legs. That, by the way, helps to reassure you that the bamboo is genuine - most wood is not hollow enough to allow that to work.

The tops of all the shelves are covered in woven cane, which is mostly in good condition. Watch out for worn areas - it is difficult and expensive to replace. C.1910, £55.

3. A sewing table, oak, painted later in cream, with berries and leaves. The top slides apart to reveal a sliding needle and thread tray over a deep well.

The sides are ornamented with machine-made fluted panels. In the original 1920s' oak, £20. Now, £35. One rare case where added decoration adds decorative value.

4. Brought down from Scotland and still in its original state, the mahogany as dark as possible to give a gleaming finish. Watch out for chipped edges which need repair. The slender legs make this table particularly attractive - too many turned legs were clumsily made. 1920s and so only £75, but good quality.

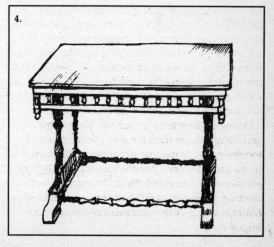

Toys and Games

A wonderful collecting field, with amusement for rainy afternoons built in! Games and toys are part of a universal memory and they cover an enormous area. The only criticism made originally by the family was when the children didn't enjoy playing with their new game. The only real regret for the collector is that the more a child plays with a toy, the more battered it becomes! Such are the ironies of collector's mania; we don't award points for survival, and the wise young child who plans to be a collector one day may have a very dull time of it at Christmas or birthdays.

COLLECTORS' NOTES

A major division can be made between automated toys and all the others. Automation does not usually include the simpler wind-up toys, like our whale, but only those which are mechanically more complex. Real automata will be almost always above our budget; they are not included.

Try to find toys with boxes, and for those always kept in boxes - like card games - it's even better if they have their original instructions.

Make sure the game is complete. Like jigsaws with one piece missing, the value of a card game, for example, missing one vital playing piece, will plummet. Learn to know what each kind should contain - how many dominoes, how many cards, and so on, and if it's something you haven't seen before, then lay it out on the table to look for any missing pieces.

Board games are particularly interesting as they are going through quite a revival. This is one case where craftsmanship, so vital to the antique collector, fails. Many games of cheap card and plastic are worth much more than another of hand-carved wood. Value depends on scarcity and often on subject. Educational games, too, are another pointer to social customs, and interest teachers and historians as well as the collector.

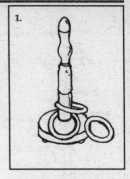

1. Quoits; there must be a hundred variations on the game of throwing rings onto a stick, and a hundred different prices for the set.

If the set is labelled, so much the better, and in its box it will bring even more. But not a rarity, and so quite a reasonable price although only for a complete boxed set, £10. If it's dated or painted with a nice design, up to £20.

2. A kaleidoscope is a source of wonder for every child, and this very simple and early example is of fine boxwood with ebony stringing.

The little flecks of paper have surprisingly kept their colour, and the whole is probably early Victorian; £30-40. Large kaleidoscopes were made with long barrels, dividing mirrors and brass fittings.

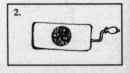

Metalware Above, an array of hip or pocket flasks in every permutation of silver plate, chrome, and a huge variety of designs. Throughout the 1920s and 1930s no gentleman would leave home without one. Looks magnificent as a display, which is warning enough. These are all reproductions and fun to own but no antique or even collector's value for another fifty years. £15–40.

Below, iron insurance plaques of the 19th century. Fun to collect, heavy to display and £15–45. Look for different companies.

Miniatures A tiny bird cage of gilded brass wire complete even down to its ceramic seed cups on either side and engraved glass shields around the base. A remarkable achievement for a model-maker, and complete with a little stuffed bird, although why it is outside and not inside is another matter. In silver, this miniature would have been at least £90, but as it's brass, even though gilded, it's a reasonable £40.

Look for sharp edges or unfinished rough undersides which would give away cheap workmanship. Probably French, and around the turn of the century, 1900–1920.

Mirrors Silver-backed handmirrors are still in plentiful supply, along with some beautiful examples in enamel on silver, and especially enamel over engine-turned silver. The dressing table sets included a mirror, a comb and brush and usually a little box for hairpins. Watch out for the same sort of display shown in the pocket flasks – i.e., a whole stall-full of reproduction mirrors. The best buys are perfect enamel ones, usually in pink, green or blue, or tortoiseshell inlaid in silver surrounds and with silver *point posé* decoration. But watch out for any chips on the borders. Prices from £15–90 for individual mirrors, up to £150 for a complete set.

Ornaments Above, a pair of sweet 18th century figures marked only with a double circle, something I have not yet been able to trace. Probably late 19th century, porcelain, £75.

Porcelain Below, an Edwardian tureen in a very pretty floral pattern, with a flowered knob. Unmarked, almost certainly English and c.1910–1920. £35.

Porcelain Above, a porcelain dish for sardines. C.1880, now hard to find, so even with no mark, not surprisingly £95. Any dish with a name on it has become fashionably collectable – especially with unusual names like this one.

Below, a small Dresden marked coffee cup and saucer with delicate fluting on both pieces. This period (1910–1920s) is between Victorian and Art Deco, so it's not been as highly prized nor as highly priced. A good tip for collectors who are willing to buy and put away, because the quality as in this little set can be superb. £50.

Pottery A pair of Japanese vases of the late 19th century. Art pottery has had a relatively low profile in Britain, with the exception of a few well-known names.

Looking East is even more fruitful in terms of future investment; this subtle and interesting style, unless by well-known potters such as Hamada, is somewhat neglected and suitably priced for bargain hunters. With crackled glaze background and impressionistic painting, £95 the pair.

A big brown and cream
jug with a well-
modelled hunting
scene (the horses and
their riders have parted
company). Not
marked, but possibly
Doulton or a
contemporary copy; the
shape is good and well
potted. £75.

Brown oil-spot lustre
jug with a silver and
pink band.
Sunderland, c.1860 and
in perfect condition, so
quite expensive, for
what is a small piece.
£95.

Prints and Etchings This very beautiful etching of a dog's head was almost certainly a portrait of a favourite pet, and because of the black border frame, quite possibly a mourning picture, too. Victorians were extremely sentimental about their pets, and this is emphasised by the fact that the artist is unknown, but the label on the back, in big letters where the artist's name and address or biographical information was usually inscribed, has only the dog's name. £65.

The fine work and very good drawing mark this out from the usual mediocre commissioned pet portraits, and it would be very interesting to do sufficient research into the artist and see if you could find other examples of his work. There are quite a few societies which have records going back to the mid-Victorian period, and there are some considerable reference books on British artists of the time which might also lead to a few clues. If baffled try to find a dealer or specialist in an auction house who knows the period – they have wide experience in obscure artists, and may well be able to set you on the right path.

More amusing and much less expensive, this period litho print had been done on aluminium sheet to emphasise the name of the product, Cycles Aluminium.

Genuine posters and advertising of this turn of the century period are increasingly hard to find and you must be very careful of reproductions which duplicate the original so well that even experts have been fooled. Metal bases like this make it more difficult to be sure, as the natural wear of paper is missing. But look for signs of use around the nail holes and scratches on the surface. £30–40 depending on picture and condition.

Silver The perfect embodiment of Art Deco design in a few inches of silver. Hallmarked 1927, this sugar sifter is simplicity itself and needs not a whiff of any kind of decoration other than its own shape. Much of the period's silver has been neglected; only in recent years, with our eyes attuned to the work of designers like Christopher Dresser and others, have we really appreciated how much austere elegance there can be in these small pieces. £85.

This neglect has been very good for collectors, but now dealers are also catching up on what the public is looking for, and Art Deco silver is rising fast in price. But one word of warning – the very simplicity makes it vulnerable. Whereas a riot of engraving or repoussé work can cover a multitude of damage, even the tiniest dent will cut the value unless you know a good silversmith who is willing to take the considerable time and trouble it will need to restore it to its pristine condition.

A pair of fish knives and forks from a much older tradition, c.1880, wonderfully elaborate and in their own way as perfect as the sifter. Unfortunately only the two pairs, not a set, so although hallmarked 1892, just £78 for the four pieces.

Souvenirs Above, an unusual souvenir in a little fan of feathers with an inscription "From Cape Town" on the back. Quite well made, the sticks are of horn, and the back unfolds to show a scene of Cape Town harbour. Probably 1930s–1940s, £32.

Left, a miniature Greek temple to hang on the wall with a mirror tucked inside; a useful souvenir for the hallway, and a constant reminder of the Parthenon in Athens, which was of course its intention. Probably c.1880 but possibly earlier, and £75 for its rarity value.

Tables Above, a very large butler's tray table of papier-mâché, made in Europe and probably decorated in Japan. The surface is in very good condition with only a few small chips at the side.

The folding separate legs are in equally good condition, with brocade straps instead of the usual webbing. C.1890–1910.

Because of its size and state, £100, and very reasonable at that price.

Right, a little miniature box for cards which turns into a table. Presumably for a drink or a dish of nuts. £15.

Toys and Games Left, a general view of a stall holding lots of goodies for the toy and game collector. Above, top, two very delightful period card games. Check that all the cards are there. The Deco designs make these more valuable. £10–15 each. Below, Domino boxes with assorted letterings. A collection can be very cheap, and great fun. Only £4–7 each.

Walking Sticks and Parasols Right, a very pretty travelling parasol with typical folding handle. The coffee coloured silk covering is fringed in pale and dark lemon, no doubt to match a particular dress. Still inexpensive at £55.

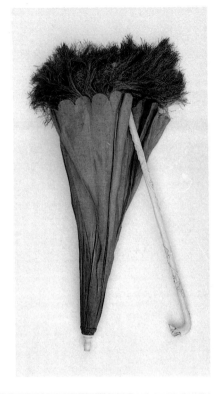

Wood I know at least five collectors who search avidly for these folding book stands. They were made during most of the Victorian period, many are of fine workmanship and carved or inlaid with rare woods, while some look almost whittled out of spare timber. A fruitful area, £35–55, and all c.1850.

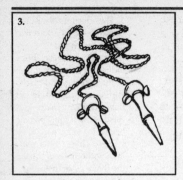

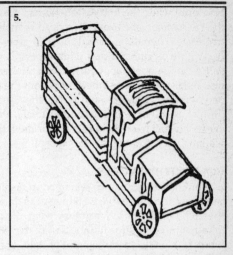

3. Skipping ropes might seem mundane, but they do vary with age and country. This pretty rope has been coloured with red and blue threads in it and the handles, badly faded now, have been painted to match.

The shape of the handles is unusual, and together with the colours, brings it to £35. Badly frayed rope or missing handles would make it worthless.

4. Boats are very common. But this one has been beautifully hand-made and named after a particular ship, probably by one of its crew for a child, which increases it value enormously. £75.

5. Toy trucks; this one was the state of the art in the 1920s. This pick-up could have carried toy sheep, sacks of sand, or little pieces of coal, a common extra sold with the cars. The truck is in reasonable condition, but the paint this time isn't faded, it was too bright! Look for traces of the original paint underneath; it's always possible that it was bought and never used, but then it should be in its box. If not, it may have repainted by a loving parent, little realising that collectors are perverse people who'd prefer it dull. £12.

6. A little bath-time whale; as the key is turned, the tail flips back and forth, sending it through the water. The key is cleverly shaped like a spout of water. Painted tin, in very good condition, end of the 19th century. Watch out for rust. Bath toys are hard to keep dry. If you do put yours in the water, then dry them in an airing cupboard or a very, very low oven afterwards. Missing keys can usually be replaced, but not one like this, so look hard to see if it's original. £40.

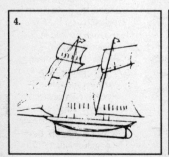

Walking Sticks and Parasols

No doubt when the first elderly human roamed the valley floor, she broke off a dead branch of a tree to help her along. Tribal societies grew to regard the ceremonial staff with respect as we still do at the opening of Parliament. Sheltering umbrellas are another inheritance from the past - once a canopy to represent the sky, they serve to protect us still at weddings and festivals, and for every day just from the weather. For men, the walking stick, for women the parasol.

COLLECTORS' NOTES

Although elaborate canes remained in fashion for centuries, the affordable walking sticks date from the mid-19th century, when they were manufactured in huge numbers until the 1920s, when fashion decreed them out of date.

The canes were usually imported separately, the handles made here or on the Continent. Silver and ivory were the most common handles, from straight simple round knobs to elaborate, semi-erotic ladies in compromising positions.

Porcelain handles are remarkable for their decorative value, but they are quite fragile, and can be collected and displayed on their own to avoid damage from handling the sticks.

Wooden handles are generally less sophisticated, many being made by country woodcarvers, although some were created by pipe makers and were later attached to a stick. Lots of examples were whittled or carved by hand as a kind of craft project - there are still competitions here for the best shepherd's walking stick.

During the 18th and 19th centuries, parasols were worn during the day in materials to suit every gown. Mourning parasols enabled even the widow to go about her respectable shopping protected from too-curious glances. Others were confections of lace and fringing with incredibly bejewelled handles that are still amazingly within our price range. Display may be difficult, but what an effect when they are all open!

1. This glorious black silk parasol is so frivolous it's hard to see it as a mourning accessory, but ladies did not use parasols in the evening, and black ruffles and lace would not have been worn during the day. So it must have been a for very merry widow. There isn't a spare inch without decoration; the inside is as ruffled as the outside. Yet only £70 will buy you this delight from the 1860s.

2. The folding handle of carriage parasols were meant to make it easy to get in and out without too much difficulty. When folded, the parasol can be tucked under the hand and then opened again when the woman is seated. Although 18th century parasols are rare and correspondingly expensive, prices for 19th century examples are very low at the moment; as low as the £40 for this green and yellow silk, c.1870.

1.

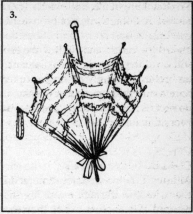

3.

3. Another parasol of the 1870s, but this time with an ivory handle inset with tiny sapphires and a blue silk covering to match.

A woman regarded her parasol as we would any possession, to be decorated as much as her own person. While jewelled handles are not quite ordinary, they are not so unusual either, and the collector today could put together a remarkable group. £95.

4. An assortment of only a few of the walking sticks which a collector can assemble in just a few months. Left to right, a carved wooden handle with panels of flowers; c.1880, £45. A slim 1930s' cane with a plain silver knob, rather beautifully shaped, and with no decoration except for another band of silver around the top of the black stick. For evening wear, £35. An ivory-headed stick with a carved lover's knot, probably from the same period; £40. A country blackthorn stick, naturally grown and just smoothed here and there to make comfortable holding. £20. An elegant handle of cream porcelain for an Edwardian dandy of c.1900, £85, attached with jade-green rings. A curved handle of a later period, perhaps 1910, with the beginnings of Art Nouveau in the silver mounting and a ring with a monogram. Finally an ivory spiral-carved head which unscrews to a small flask for brandy or whisky. £97, and the scent of brandy for free.

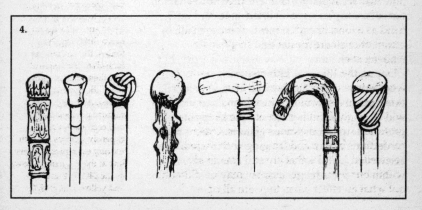

4.

Wine Collectables

The drinking of alcoholic beverages has a long history and there's no doubt that the first collector wasn't far behind. Food and drink are necessary for life and so they are necessary to our social history as well. Breaking bread together has great meaning; drinking a cup of wine together perhaps even more. In any case, wine, its production, its storing and its serving have become a subject full of interest and variety.

COLLECTORS' NOTES

Corkscrews first appeared at the end of the 17th century, as wine was stored in reclining bottles; the wine kept the cork moist, and it had to be pushed in very hard, which then made it harder to remove when required.

Early examples were either heavy iron and very crude or silver, and these are now way beyond our limit. But from 1795, when the first patent was registered, there emerged such a forest of these indispensable gadgets that the collector is truly spoiled. Few reach beyond £80 or £100; most cost between £30 and £60. There is an entire science of when each improvement or new invention was patented and sold to an eager public which the new collector would do well to investigate.

Labels are another fruitful area for collectors; they were mainly intended for decanters at home and they were made mainly in silver and enamel, again in a wide variety of styles and names. The unusual labels bring the most, or those made by a well-regarded silversmith.

Silver wine funnels are available at a price, but silver plate ones are within our budget.

For interesting ideas at lower cost, look for the oddities; labels from famous vintages, posters and ephemera about wine, old books, prints, etc. One of the associated wine collector's areas might be decanters, and these are covered in a separate section; look also for additional glasses in that section, and for drinking cups in Silver.

1. For the person who preferred not to need a corkscrew, these silver-topped corks were a wonderful invention. The label on top is engraved within a silver disc, but there are porcelain tops as well, some with quite elaborate paintings. This one dates from 1924, but they were made quite recently too, as well as in the late 19th century for homes with not enough decanters to cater for every drink.

Once you have started, you might find it more intriguing to concentrate on one particular drink, like port. There are port glasses, port decanters, port labels, posters for port, histories of the vineyards which produce port, relics of Oporto and the English colony which was responsible for so much of port's popularity with the British people. Start with this cork, at around £22, hallmarked London.

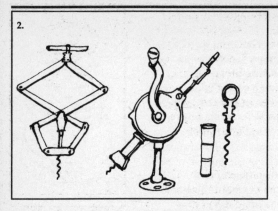

2.

4.

2. When Edward Thomason of Birmingham brought out his double-action patented corkscrew in 1802, he could hardly imagine that 180 years later one would sell for over £100. But so it is. And rightly so, because similar screws remained in production well into this century. From the mid-19th century, though, the production of corkscrews exploded, and there are almost as many systems or inventions are there are models. Some are spectacularly mechanical like the concertina screw, left; some were made ultra-heavy and sturdy to be screwed first into a pub or restaurant table like centre above, and some were so tiny they could slip into a pencil and be stored in a gentleman's coat pocket, right, above.

Find out about the rare trade names - they aren't always the very earliest ones. A 1870s patent called the Holborn Lever is eagerly sought after by collectors.

Look for specific types, like the pocket models, or pub models, or steel spring models from the 1830s on. There are many German corkscrews with some complicated workings and quite a few with a little brush to clear away any cork debris. Prices above: left, £70; centre, £45; right, £80.

4. Wine coasters were meant to protect the polished wood of the table, but they also served to coast the bottles along when port was served to the men. Silver coasters usually have mahogany bases, ridged to let any drips collect below the bottle. 1934, £32, Chester.

5. Art Deco cocktail shaker in chrome, with red and black enamelling. Perfect condition, c.1932, £40. Check that tops fit.

3. A selection of labels make an attractive display, easy to show off in a glass-covered table.

Be careful of chipped enamel edges. While the name may be rare and unusual, it will be down-graded by poor condition, much more than dented silver, which can be repaired. C.1910, £30-55.

3.

5.

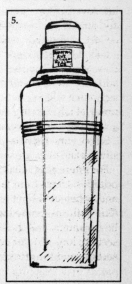

Wood

Treen is the word used to describe small objects of wood, probably from the Old English word for tree. Nowadays there are some collectors of wooden things who would not recognise the word nor probably the little objects either, because since the revival of kitchen and garden crafts, many wood collectors tend to go for the bigger and more exotic pieces - utensils from the dairy or farmyard, or working tools from a hundred different professions, but all sharing a respect and a high regard for the beauty of our oldest and most varied natural resource.
There are wooden objects throughout this book, but I've gathered here some of my favourites.

COLLECTORS' NOTES

As a material, wood suffers from a multiplicity of problems; it is badly rotted by damp, split by heat, eaten by insects and consumed by fire. And yet throughout the history of our planet it has served us so well that we are willing to take time and trouble to keep protecting it.

Wood falls generally into two categories, hard and softwood. Hardwoods include mahogany, oak, beech, rosewood and teak; they are deciduous and broad-leafed trees. Softwoods are mostly varieties of pine, spruce, fir, etc. which are needle-leafed conifers.

The grain in hardwood is dense, which makes it harder to work and to carve, but in fact pine, a softwood, is more stable than mahogany or oak, which is why many large pieces of furniture are made on a pine base with a hardwood veneer for its more decorative appearance.

Veneers, thin slices of decorative woods including stained colours and grains, have been used for 4,000 years. The earlier the veneer, the thicker; today's machines can take off the thinnest slivers of wood which still retain their pattern and colour.

Wood has its own protection, a patina from continual polishing or natural oils. Damaging the patina may take fifty years to repair.

1. A new respect for the work of our predecessors has brought new life to many old utensils. Butter churns were made of oak staves coopered like a barrel, with a round top pierced by a long paddle, probably of birch or pine. Everything had to be kept scrupulously clean, and churns were scrubbed down between each milking and subsequent butter making.

After the butter had formed it was patted into shape and turned into wooden pails like this, to be stored in the cold dairy or larder. Sycamore wood was favoured for its lack of oil which avoided adding any taste to the butter.

Although never polished, the years have their own effect and well-used pails turn a lovely golden ash colour which no modern stain can match. Watch out for loose hoops and cracked handles which are hard to repair. 1920s, £75.

2.

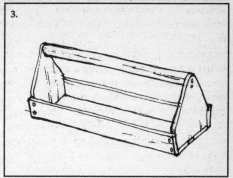

3.

2. Agricultural measures are large and unwieldy, but these two grain measures from French Canada were probably used in a retail store rather than on a farm. Both are now dark brown with age, the letters burnt into the oak and almost gone again from polishing, the hoops hand-wrought black iron. Collecting the rest of the set is an ambition of mine. More sophisticated measures have a handle and some are marked on the outside with varying quantities. Dated 1876, £45 and £65. French ones were once rare in England, but the same pattern was used everywhere in that period, and with the number of English people visiting and shopping in France, you may well find an identical set.

3. The long carrier is more unusual and one I've not seen before. It was made in East Anglia c.1900 to carry the first punnets of soft fruit to market; it holds six large punnets, and it is very light to carry. A soft brown birch this time, and neatly nailed together. Look for the irregular tops of hand-made nails, no new wood showing from recent re-nailing. 1900s, £45.

4. A real collector's piece, a plane with a steel plate and a teak handle, made in 1880 by Spiers and Co. of Ayr and in absolutely perfect condition, ready to use tomorrow.

Tools are a new collector's area, but you must understand the market because each profession has its own set of values and assessment criteria.

Old catalogues are some of the best sources of descriptions and pictures. If held correctly even by a novice good tools usually feel comfortable - the sign of craftsmanship in the making. This particular plane is a scarce model, and it will bring £85.

5. Even serious wood-workers have a sense of humour. This mad chicken picks up cigarettes with its beak. Patterned everywhere in parquetry, probably German, 1930s, £15.

5.

4.

Glossary: An Antiques ABC

This glossary contains those terms which might be most puzzling, or occur often in catalogues or articles and which are not in general use, or are explained elsewhere in the text. For reasons of space it cannot possibly be comprehensive, and it has to reflect those areas which we believe will be helpful and intriguing. Many other words and definitions will be found in specialist publications, in large general dictionaries and in good encyclopaedias which we recommend to all fervent collectors.

Alloy
Any mixture of metals.

Annealing
Glass is an unstable material, and it has to be made more stable by slow heating and controlled cooling in an annealing oven. Badly annealed glass will crack and fall apart.

Antimony
A metal used to harden Britannia Metal.

Apron
Shaped piece below a table top, under a seat or below the bottom shelf of a cabinet. It can be highly carved and decorative.

Arcade
A repetitive arch used as a border on silver, ceramics, etc.

Baby doll
Not always what it implies! In Britain, a doll dressed as a baby, but in France, any doll which represents a young person as opposed to a grown-up doll.

Baguette
A rectangular gemstone, often used to encircle a single round stone, or in a series of geometric designs in Art Deco jewellery.

Benchwork
Work on cold metal, instead of work at the forge. See **Lampwork** for similar technique on glass.

Berlin wool
A soft untwisted embroidery wool imported from Germany in the mid-19th century, along with coloured charts; they popularised home embroidery because the wool was thick and easy to work and the charts were easy to use.

Bevel
The slanted edge of a flat surface which marks the change from one level to another. Until recently the edges of good quality mirrors were always bevelled.

Bezel
The metal frame around the glass of a clock or watch.

Bisque
Primarily unglazed ceramic left in its natural colour, a flesh pink. Used by doll collectors to mean flesh-coloured china dolls, unglazed, and with a matt surface.

Black work
Embroidery much used in the 16th and 17th centuries, of black threads on white linen; it was revived during the mediaeval passion of the 19th century, and pieces of that can be found quite often today.

Blown moulded
Blown moulding has been part of fine glassware since Roman times. To decorate any hollow ware with relief patterns, a bubble of glass is blown into a two or three part mould and removed quickly, to be finished by hand. The inside of the object will follow the contours of the design. See **Pressed glass** for machine-made moulding.

Bracket clock
An English clock type, driven by springs and *not* usually on bracket feet. What we call a bracket clock is a mantelpiece clock, which usually did stand on a bracket.

Bright cut
Engraving with a highly polished tool so that the edges are shiny and reflect light.

Very popular in the 18th and 19th centuries.

Cabochon
A rounded, dome-cut jewel, used in the l9th century for revival antique designs, and later with coloured stones in real and costume jewellery - large cabochon glass rubies, for example, look magnificent where highly cut ones might look cheap.

Cameo
Generally a gemstone or a shell which has been carved in layers to create an image with a three-dimentional appearance.

Also layers of glass which are carved in the same way. The Portland Vase is probably the most famous piece of cameo glass carving, made in ancient Rome, and copied c.1850 by John Northwood. Cameo in glass was also adopted by French artists such as Emile Gallé.

Cane
A thick group of differently coloured glass rods, or just opaque white and clear rods, are gathered together in a circular pattern and themselves encased in clear glass. The cane is then heated and pulled out to a thickness no bigger than a pencil, allowed to cool, and then chopped either into tiny slices to make up into paperweights or into short rods for glass stems.

Canteen
A case with a full service of flatware in a box. Middle-class Edwardian and between-the-wars brides expected a full canteen of silver or plate as part of their wedding gifts.

Carriage clock
Once a term for little clocks that were portable enough to be carried from place to place and to go in the coach on long journeys. Now it refers to any small clock, usually rectangular in shape, with handles at the sides and perhaps a leather case. Many had repeating levers to tell the time in the dark, so they are particularly popular nowadays as bedroom clocks.

Cartouche
A space within a border, usually filled with an inscription, etc. The border can be quite decorative, and it was much used in map-making hence its derivation from carte and our word cartography.

Casting
Any metal made molten, poured into a mould and allowed to cool before being turned out and finished. In iron and brass work, entire articles were often cast, but in silver and gold it was usually the small added parts which were cast, like handles, ornamentation, or mass-produced jewellery settings, all difficult and expensive to manipulate by hand.

Castors
Small wheels on the legs of heavy furniture to allow it to be easily moved. Originally in leather or porcelain, they were generally made of brass or bronze in Victorian times. They look very awkward on any furniture with delicate or splayed legs.

Chapter ring
The circular ring which contains the figures for the hours on a clockface. It can be metal, enamel, etc. In modern clocks the chapter ring has merged into the face.

Chasing
Decorating any metal by pushing it into high or low relief, as in embossing and repoussé, all of which are very similar; i.e., repoussé is produced by first embossing, then chasing.

China clay
This is the best clay for porcelain, and it comes from decomposed granite. When china clay and china stone are blended and fired together at around 1350 degrees farenheit, it forms hard-paste porcelain.

Chopin
An old Scottish measure, often found in pewter or brass.

Glossary

Clockwork
Any mechanism operated by a spring which is wound up. It can be a clock, a toy, etc.

Commode
We think of this as a chair with a chamber pot under the seat, but it's also a highly decorative chest of drawers, so don't be misled by auction descriptions either way.

Crackle
A deliberately induced form of decoration with a network of fine cracks over the glaze, but also to give the impression of great age. It was popular on Chinese pieces and those inspired by them in the 19th and 20th centuries.

Crazed
A glaze which has shrunk too much and cracked. Applied to ceramic glazes, and to the faces of wax dolls which often suffer the same fate. **Crackle** is deliberate crazing.

Crizzled
Glass "sickness" called crizzling is indicated when a network of tiny cracks break apart the surface, flake off and eventually destroy the entire object. Crizzling applies mainly to old glass imperfectly annealed in the kiln. See **Crackle** and **Ice glass** for what might be called deliberate crizzling.

Damascene
Decoration of iron or steel by inlaying with gold and silver, from Damascus where the best quality was made.

Delft
The centre of production in Holland of blue and white earthenware inspired originally by Chinese porcelain, but then recreated with European motifs in one of the greatest outpourings of national style the ceramic world has ever known. Beloved of all country kitchen collectors and imitated by almost every bad pottery factory, modern Delftware has flooded the tourist market with trinkets which are worthless now, but may be prized in two or three hundred years. Some very fine work is still being produced but it's a minefield since Dutch potters copied old marks in the same way that Chinese potteries did, and attribution is difficult and full of pitfalls until you know the styles and the techniques of different potters. Although prices are rising rapidly, it is ironic that fine Dutch Delft of the 18th and 19th centuries was little regarded here, selling ten years ago for £40-50 while English copies were being sold for very high prices. This is an area of possibilities for the collector on a budget but it had better be soon.

Distressed
A euphemism for any surface, but particularly in wood and furniture, which has been deliberately mistreated to create an impression of age; beating with chains, scattering with ink stains, roughening a smooth surface have all been used. Even new ceramic tiles are cracked and gouged out in places and called distressed to simulate old farmhouse floor tiles.

Dyes
Almost all the dyes of the 19th century were natural ones from plant and animal materials. After c.1848 chemical dyes became prevalant because they were more reliable and cheaper to make.

Embossing: see Chasing

Enamel
Enamel is a form of coloured glass which is used to decorate ceramics, metals, etc. When it is painted on ceramics, it is always put on after the original piece has been fired with a glaze; high temperature for porcelain, a lower temperature for earthenware. Some decoration, like transfer printing and cobalt blue painting are done as soon as the clay body has dried. The pot is dipped in a transparent glaze and then fired in one process. Enamel painting is not strong enough to withstand such high heat. It is painted on top of the already-glazed piece and fired at a much lower

temperature, in a muffle kiln. There are comparatively few colours which can withstand the high heat of the original porcelain kiln. The development of brilliant enamel colouring in China early in the 18th century revolutionised the decoration of all ceramics as well as enamelling on copper (the colours known as Famille Rose, Famille Noir, Famille Jaune, etc., are all enamel colours).

Engine turning
Engraving or chasing with a machine to give a distinctive all-over pattern. It's much older than generally realised, dating back to the mid-18th century, and it was used by Norwegians and Russians with translucent enamel coating over gilt or silver engine-turned designs (see Spoons section) and also much used by Fabergé - not shown in this book! Very popular from the 1930s to the 1950s on all metals used for cigarette lighters, cases, etc. as it resists any marking from continual handling.

Engraving
Cutting grooves into any metal or hard surface. The effect is the opposite of embossing which raises the metal. Also a print taken from an engraved plate. See also **Intaglio.**

Escapement
A controlling mechanism in the movement of a clock which regulates the escape of each tooth in the wheel as it rotates, and is itself controlled by the balance or the pendulum. The earliest escapements, the verge and the anchor, had a slight recoil as the tooth was caught, making the time-keeping facility less accurate. Modern escapements, including those used for watches i.e. the lever, the cylinder and the duplex, have no recoil and the movements are more accurate as a result.

Escutcheon
In the decorative arts, a shield with the coat of arms or any armorial bearings. In locksmithery, the pivoting cover of the keyhole, often finely decorated in the past, although now usually a simple brass or other metal plate.

Faience: see **Tin glazes**

Figure
The pattern in wood, especially in veneer. Burr walnut is highly figured, rosewood is generally not.

Finial
The finishing touch! An ornament for the top of something - usually a lamp or the centre of a tall cabinet - which comes to a point. A finishing motif on the top of a spoon, for example.

Flatware
Tablewares such as spoons and forks with no cutting edge and therefore theoretically excluding knives, but today it's used to mean all general tableware, even carving knives and forks.

Foundry, founder
A foundry is a place for casting metals, the founder is a skilled craftsperson working there.

Foxing
Spots of mould which appear on old printed or painted paper. While a little foxing is acceptable, more than that reduces the value of the paper. It can be removed, albeit by very careful cleaning by a professional.

French polish
Varnish used since the early 19th century to save effort in polishing. A kind of shellac is used to coat the wood in several layers, and the result is an artificial and shiny appearance, very out of favour at the moment.

Much early furniture was inappropriately French polished by the Victorians, ruining the original patina, and destroying a lot of its present value.

Glossary

Gadroon
A kind of chain decoration of slanted oval mounds, much used in Venetian glass and almost all silver, as well as around the edges of some ceramic decorative plates.

Gilding
The application of gold to any ware. Silver was often washed with gold (silver gilt) not just for decoration but to protect against tarnishing from acid in food. Gilding on ceramics or glass is done after the object is finished and glazed. Gold is mixed - originally with honey but since the 1780s with mercury - and fired in the low temperature muffle kiln before being burnished by wheel or by hand. When gilding is rubbed away it often leaves a trace of its fixative in a light white shadow on the glass or china. Gilding on wood or metal is put on as gold leaf and burnished in the same way.

Gnomon
The art of making sundials was originally called dialing, or gnomics. We use the word to refer to the shadow-casting part of the dial, although technically it's only the point of the style which is a gnomon.

Grandfather and Grandmother clocks
These are what are known less sentimentally as long case clocks, the Grandmother being shorter at under six feet tall.

Green glass
So much bottle glass is green that it has been assumed there were all sorts of reasons, such as keeping food safe from sunlight, etc. But the green comes from iron oxide present in almost all sand, one of the main components of glass. Decolourisers have to be used, often based on manganese, to make it clear, and so the cheapest and most ordinary bottles are left green.

Ice glass
A very popular Victorian technique of deliberately creating a crackled surface on the glass, much as Chinese ceramics have a crackled background. Not to be confused with crizzling, it does the glass no harm and is created by dipping hot glass in cold water.

Imari
A vivid and brilliantly busy style of decoration of Japanese derivation often called the brocade pattern, based on red and gold laid on a blue and white design. It was shipped to Europe from Imari harbour hence its name. The designs have become a collectors' field, regardless of origin, something like blue and white. The style was imitated on the Continent during the 18th and 19th centuries, and most affordably by the Royal Crown Derby factory c.1820s right up to the present day. It remains one of their most popular group of patterns; check the date marks carefully if you are interested in dishes from Robert Bloor's period as owner, c.1811-1840.

Impasto
As in painting, any surface colour or texture applied thickly and unevenly.

Inro and Netsuke
The most popular form of Japanese collectables, inro are small boxes which fit together on a cord and are hung from a sash with a netsuke, or carved toggle, on the other end to keep them from being pulled off. The netsuke are miraculous miniature carvings generally of ivory, bone or wood, although other materials can be used. Any and all subjects were used to suit the customer. Inro are small and incredibly wonderful boxes of fine lacquer with compartments for medicine, for cosmetics, for anything a man or woman might need. The finest are very expensive indeed, but they were produced in very large quantities and so occasionally show up at house sales, etc. brought back as souvenirs. As they were often made together, a pair would have the inro still connected to the netsuke by its cord. The best affordable examples are late 19th and early 20th centuries.

Intaglio
Carving into a material, originally gems or glass, to give an image which will usually be seen only when used in reverse. For example, a seal is intaglio work - you see the image when the seal is pressed into wax. The reverse of cameo work where the background is cut away to leave the picture in relief, Intaglio can be used inside ceramic moulds so that when the clay is turned out there are motifs in relief on the surface.

Japanning
Mistakenly confused with genuine lacquer, japanning was popular in the 19th century when factories used a hard varnish called japan to simulate Japanese black lacquer.

Kewpie
A celluloid doll of small size with a "cute" expression. Originally made in America c.1911 as one of the cheapest dolls and synonymous with fairground prizes, etc.

Kick
The hollow under the foot. In an old glass it surrounds the pontil mark.

Knop
Another word for knob, referring to small bumps of various shapes and sizes which break the straight line of a glass stem.

Lampwork
Work done in manipulating small amounts of glass over a small flame lamp rather than at the furnace. Similar to benchwork for metal workers. Glass animals and paperweight bases are lampwork.

Latticinio
Originally an old Venetian technique for embedding rods of white or coloured glass woven into a lacy pattern in clear glass. Very popular again in the 1940s and 1950s in plates, vases and for compôtes.

Lustre wares
Lustre has been a favourite of the British potters since the 18th century, but it really came into its own with the Staffordshire potters of the 19th century and later. The gleaming effect is created by using a special kiln called a reduction kiln. This achieves a very smoky atmosphere at a lowish temperature, so it is especially suitable for earthenwares. Metallic colourings are used, and in the kiln, the oxygen in the clay combines with the metals to create a shimmering range of colours, according to the metallic oxides used. Copper fires to copper colour (one of the favourites) while silver oxide fires to a brassy yellow; gold chloride looks like copper on a dark brown background and like pink on a white clay. Platinum has to be used to make silver colour.

Maiolica, Majolica: see Tin Glazes

Metal
Aside from its obvious meaning, for some reason difficult to understand the actual material, glass, is referred to by collectors and makers as metal while the object is a glass; e.g. "the metal of ethnic glass is often full of imperfections and little stones". Very confusing.

Millefiori
Italian for a thousand flowers, and first used mid-19th century to describe the kinds of paperweights which have slices of many different **canes** on their bases (which see). It also refers to ceramic patterns with scatterings of many tiny flowers over a white ground.

Overlay
Used to describe a glass with layers of different colours which are cut away to create an illusion of depth and tone. Also called cased glass.

Paktong
An amalgam of copper, nickel and zinc, which looks like polished steel, much used in Victorian times for fireplace furniture, etc. Sometimes called German silver.

Glossary

Papier-mâché
Layers of paper shredded into a pulp and then pressed into a shape. Sometimes it is made over a wood core. When really dry it can be treated just like wood, and it was used for all sorts of trinkets and small furniture. Particularly popular in England and Germany from c.1770-1885 in the familiar painted black lacquer imitations.

Parian
A type of very fine, smooth porcelain developed probably by Copeland's c.1845 and generally unglazed and left matt white. It was used to make marble-like figures and busts, and originally called statuary porcelain but later it was sometimes coloured and even salt glazed. It also refers to some dolls with white unglazed china heads, arms and feet.

Patina
The surface of wood when it has been polished and waxed for generations. It can be faked, but not easily when the wood has turned a particularly rich colour. French polishing destroys the patina by putting on a coat of shellac - the best treatment for fine wood is still beeswax and elbow grease. The word has been adopted by other kinds of antique dealers to describe old and well-cared for finishes - brass (only unlacquered, or you have the same effect as French polishing), copper, bronze and even leather are described as having a good or pleasant patina.

Pendulum
The suspended object in a clock which regulates and controls all the movements. The shaft is called the rod and the weight is called the bob. Some long case clocks have had their old pendulums replaced.

Pinchbeck
An alloy of zinc and mainly copper used in the 18th and 19th centuries to imitate gold. It was invented by a Mr Pinchbeck, and the little boxes, trinkets and especially 19th century jewellery is now so collectable that the word is proudly used in descriptions whenever possible. The colour is quite red, and it's very soft.

Piqué point
A form of decoration where tiny dots of metal, usually silver but also copper and gold, were embedded into softened tortoiseshell, horn or ivory. When the material dried, it tightened around the metal and held it firmly in place. 19th century piqué point was used extensively on little boxes, on hair combs, etc. Later the same technique was used on plastic handbag and combs with exactly the same delightful effect.

Plaster of Paris
Very fine white gypsum which swells rapidly in water and sets quickly. Used for making moulds in ceramics, and sometimes mistakenly bought as stone.

Plate metal
Pewter which is of the very best quality.

Poker work
Decoration on plain wood made by burning lines and dots with a hot poker. Very popular as a home craft in late Victorian times and found today at car boot sales and charity shops in great abundance.

Pontil or punty mark
While a glass is being finished off, it's held at the foot by a heavy iron rod called the pontil, or punty. When the worker has finished, the glass is allowed to cool slightly to make sure it's set and then it's knocked off sharply into a bed of sand, leaving a jagged edge underneath the foot. 18th century glassmen left this pontil mark on, since the foot was domed and it never touched the table or the cloth. When the 19th century styles were made with the new flatter feet, the pontil mark was ground down. The lack or presence of a pontil mark is sometimes used to identify old glasses, but new marks can easily be

made exactly like an antique, since the methods of hand-blowing have not changed at all. However, its absence does help to establish a likely 19th century date.

Pressed glass
Machine moulded glassware was developed primarily in America for mass production. Multiple moulds can be filled at one time by molten or liquid glass, an interior plug is lowered into the mould and the glass is allowed to set . Then the plug is pulled up and the moulds fall open, leaving the pressed glass shape. You can almost always see the two or three lines around the outside, and the inside will be completely smooth with no relationship to the outside design.

Salt glaze
One of the earliest known ceramic glazes, made by throwing salt into the kiln at the hottest moment in the firing. It dissolves in the heat into a tough, pitted glaze often referred to as "orange peel" which is particularly attractive on stoneware, although it has very occasionally been used on porcelain.

Sand-box
A small container of sand, having a perforated top so the sand could be sprinkled on ink to make it dry quickly. Also called a pounce box, which contained powered pumice stone for the same purpose. Usually in silver or pewter, but I have seen them in glass as well.

Slip
Liquid clay of a creamy consistency which can be used for decoration by dipping dark bodies in light slip, or vice versa, or trailed over the pot in a free-hand design. It can also be used to create intricate moulded designs by being poured in thin layers and allowed to dry.

Splat
The central upright rising from the chair seat to the rail.

Stipple, stippled
A form of decoration made by tiny dots in an overall pattern. Also used in engraving for backgrounds.

Stretcher
Any rail running between the legs of a chair or table to reinforce it.

Striae
Ripples in glass which are not imperfections as such, but which are formed when the glass hasn't been properly melted before being used.

Thread
A thin trail of slip in ceramics or glass wrapped around the stem or the bowl.

Tin glazes
One of the most important glazes in the history of ceramics. Tin oxide, added to a clear lead glaze, becomes a beautiful opaque white. The early tin glazes on Spanish pottery (imported into Italy through Majorca) inspired the Italians who copied it to make brilliantly coloured objects which are now called maiolica. Then in the late 19th century came the Arts and Crafts movement and potters like William de Morgan, reviving the technique to make English Majolica; relief-decorated tiles, in thick rich jewel tones, garden furniture and heavily glazed and swirled dishes of the period.

Delft in Holland (which see) became a centre of very different tin-glazed ware in the 17th and 18th centuries. Faience is just another name for tin-glazed ware made in the styles of France and Germany.

Touch
The personal mark used by pewterers to identify their own pieces. Silver marks of similar origin are called maker's marks.

Trio
Refers to a cup, a saucer and a small plate in the same pattern and sold together.

Ward

The cut pattern on the end of a key which is designed to ensure that no other key will turn the lock; also its corresponding levers or falls inside the lock.

Wrythen

An irregular, twisting decoration which flows around and up a glass or a vase. Used especially in dwarf ale glasses, but also in vases.

By leaving out some classic books which have been long out of print and difficult to find we have tried to ensure that the books listed here should be in print, or at least on the shelves of a good library with a comprehensive section on the arts.

Look under your chosen subject in the reference section of the library catalogue or in Books in Print for current publications. If neither give you the information you need, ask about specialist book dealers who have new and secondhand books on antiques.

The books are listed alphabetically by title, since many have multiple authors, and in any case a new collector is more likely to remember the name of the book than the author.

Please note that most reference books do not deal with prices, and few price guides offer much information about objects costing under £100. But both will give you information on the subject that will be useful in assessing date and characteristics, and which should stand you in good stead when looking at smaller items.

Many reference books cover a wide variety of subjects but not necessarily in the way we have divided them in the contents, so here look under Furniture if you are interested in Tables , Chairs or Shelves (there are few if any single books on those subjects) or in an amalgamated section like Pottery and Porcelain for all ceramic books. And if the subject you want isn't mentioned, try the big encyclopedias and dictionaries.

If you have difficulty in tracking down the publisher of an out-of-print book, The Bookseller in Dyott Street, London is part of the company which publishes Books in Print and they can usually trace the name you want. Many books on antiques are well-established classics in their field, and have bveen reprinted by different publishers and in other editions. If you have any difficulty please let me know.

General Dictionaries, Encyclopedias, and Reference Books

The Antiques Collecting Directory
Lorraine Johnson; 1983, Pan Books, London.

Collins Encyclopedia of Antiques
1973, William Collins & Sons, London
A basic dictionary providing precise definitions. Hard to find now and admittedly restricted to traditional areas of collecting (no biscuit tins, for example). Bibliography.

The Complete Encyclopedia of Antiques
1973, Ebury Press, London.
Background and pictures for sixteen major areas of traditional collecting. Specialised books list.

The Concise Encyclopedia of Antiques
The Connoisseur; 1970, Ebury Press, London.
Both an earlier five-volume set of articles from The Connoisseur *Magazine, and a single volume Encyclopedia later. All written by the best experts of the time, but on traditional antique areas only, and in many cases out of date in terms of new knowledge from academic studies in the past twenty years. However, a mine of information to fill out your knowledge.*

Dictionary of Antiques
George Savage; 1970, Barrie and Jenkins, London
A classic reference book, still full of good things, from a great expert.

Reference Book List

Treasures in Your Home
1993 The Readers' Digest
Association Ltd, London
*Newest book filled with information
including many of the less traditional
areas. Unfortunately almost all of the
examples shown are more expensive
than our budget allows but it does
provide background.*

Price Guides

**The Lyle Official Antiques
Review**
The Book People, Godalming
Surrey
*One of three annual price guides,
including many less traditional
subjects.*

Miller's Antiques Price Guides
and
Miller's Collectables Price Guides
Yearly editions from Miller's
Publications, Tenterden, Kent
The Collectables *series is particularly
useful but the prices are not our budget
level!*

**The Which? Guide to Buying
Collectables: The Essential Price
Guide to Hundreds of Small
Antiques and Bygones**
Duncan Chilcott; 1991, Consumer's
Association & Hodder and
Stoughton, London
*Very well illustrated with good
photographs and background material,
but small does not mean inexpensive.*

Reading List By Subject

The following pages list titles which
*relate to the different areas in the book.
Sometimes there are no specific
recommendations - as far as I am
aware, for example, there are no
straightforward books on fireplace
furniture or inexpensive garden
ornaments - and in other cases there
are so many books that we have been
able to mention only a few.*

*In either case look also through the
big encyclopedias and reference books,
as well as the price guides, under other
possible subjects, such as marbles,
statues, brass or metalware.*

*Some publishers specialise in the
antiques world - the Antique
Collector's Club based in Woodbridge,
Suffolk is particularly good for
background reading, although their
books do concentrate on the more
expensive objects.*

*Christie's and Sotheby's
publications, although their
programmes have been more selective
lately, are always good value for
learning about current trends at the
higher levels. Their yearbooks also help
to keep you in touch with the market.*

*Many home and decorating
magazines now carry articles regularly
on antiques subjects.*

*Probably the most useful series for
the beginner are the small booklets put
out by Shire Publications. No prices
but good basic history from some of the
leading experts, with interesting
sidelines and exceptionally useful
illustrations. They cover all sorts of
minor collectables as well, from
shoehorns to thimbles, and at a very
modest cost they are marvellous value.*

Style Guides

Art Deco
Victor Arwas; 1980, Abrams, New York

Art Nouveau Collectables
Philippe Garner; 1974, Hamlyn, London

Contemporary Decorative Arts from 1940 to the present day
Philippe Garner; 1980, Phaidon, Oxford

Decorative Art 1880-1980
Dan Klein and Margaret Bishop; 1986, Phaidon Christie's, Oxford.

The Decorative Twenties
Martin Battersby; 1969, 1988 Whitney, New York

The Liberty Style
1979, Academy Editions, London

Lyle Price Guide Art Nouveau and Deco
Tony Curtis; 1992, Lyle Publications, Scotland

Miller's Antiques Checklist series:
Art Deco, Art Nouveau, Victoriana, Facts File, Pocket Dictionary
M. Miller; 1991-94, all published by Mitchell Beazley, London.
The World of Edwardiana
Philippe Garner; 1974, Hamlyn, London

Also look at various series from Christie's, Sotheby's, Guinness, Hamlyn, etc. which include a number of relevant titles.

Animals

Animals in Pottery and Porcelain
John Cushion; 1976, Studio Vista, London

Antique Cats
Katherine Whitehall
Studio Vista, London

Artists' Collectables

Drawing Instruments
Michael Scott-Scott; Shire Publications, Princes Risborough, Bucks.

Baskets

Baskets and Basketmaking
Shire Publications, Princes Risborough, Bucks

Beads

Beads
Joan Edwards; 1976, Batsford, London

Beadwork
Pamela Clabburn; Shire Publications, Princes Risborough, Bucks

Bottles

Bottles and Bottle Collecting
A. Hedges; Shire Publications, Princes Risborough, Bucks

See also under Glass

Reference Book List

Baby and Child
Memories of Childhood
1992, Bracken Books, London

Boxes
Boxes
Brian Cole, 1975; Pitman, London

Clocks and Watches
The Country Life Book of Watches
Camera Cuss; 1967, Country Life

The Price Guide to Clocks 1840-1940
Alan and Rita Shenton; 1985, The Antique Collectors' Club, Woodbridge, Suffolk

Dolls
The Collector's Encyclopedia of Dolls
Coleman; 1972, Robert Hale, London

Dolls and Doll Houses
Constance Eileen King; 1977, Hamlyn, London

Paper Dolls and Paper Toys
Barbara Whitton, rev. 1980; Jendrick, USA

Embroidery and Linen
Ayrshire and other Whitework
Margaret Swain; Shire publications, Princes Risborough, Bucks

Collecting Antique Linens, Lace and Needlework: Identification,

Restoration and Prices
Frances Johnson; 1991, Wallace Homestead, Radnor, Pennsylvania.

Crewel Embroidery
Joan Edwards; 1976, Batsford, London

Crochet
Pauline Turner; Shire publications, Princes Risborough, Bucks

Discovering 19th Century Embroidery
Santina Levey; Shire Publications, Princes Risborough, Bucks

Encyclopedia of Needlework
Pamela Clabburn; 1975, Macmillan Press, London

Furniture
Dictionary of Country Furniture
Marjorie Filbee; 1977, The Connoisseur, London

The Englishman's Chair
John Gloag; 1964, Allen and Unwin

Oak Furniture: The British Tradition
Victor Chinnery; 1979, Antique Collectors' Club, Woodbridge Suffolk

The Price Guide to Victorian, Edwardian and 1920s Furniture
John Andrews; 1980, prices updated since, Antique Collectors' Club, Woodbridge, Suffolk

Victorian Furniture
Simon Jarvis; 1968, Barrie and
Jenkins, London

World Furniture
Helena Hayward, ed; 1965, Spring
Books

Glass
Carnival Glass
Raymond Notley; Shire
Publications, Princes Risborough,
Bucks.

Contemporary Art Glass
Ray and Lee Grover; 1975, Crown,
New York

The Encyclopedia of Glass
Phoebe Phillips, ed.; 1982,
Heinemann

**English Bottles and Decanters to
1900**
Derek Davis; 1972, World
Publications

An Illustrated Dictionary of Glass
Harold Newman; 1977, Thames
and Hudson, London

Nineteenth Century British Glass
Hugh Wakefield; 1961, Faber and
Faber

Pressed Flint Glass
Raymond Notley; Shire
Publications, Princes Risborough,
Bucks

Victorian Table Glass
Betty Bradford; 1976, Herbert
Jenkins, London

Jewellery
The Arts and Crafts Movement
Gillian Naylor; 1971, Thames and
Hudson, London

**Cut Steel and Berlin Ironwork
Jewellery**
Anne Clifford; 1973, Bath

**European and American Jewellery
1830-1914**
Charlotte Gere; 1975, Heinemann,
London

A History of Jewellery, 1100-1870
Joan Evans; rev. 1970, Batsford,
London

**An Illustrated Dictionary of
Jewellery**
Harold Newman; 1982, Thames
and Hudson, London

Jet Jewellery and Ornaments
Helen Muller; Shire Publications,
Princes Risborough, Bucks`

**Jewellery; An Historical Survey of
British Styles and Jewels**
Nancy Armstrong; 1963, Barrie and
Jenkins, London

Modern Jewellery
G. Hughes; 1964, Studio Vista,
London

Kitchenware
Domestic Bygones
J. Fearn; Shire Publications, Princes
Risborough, Bucks

Reference Book List

Fire Grates and Kitchen Ranges
David Eveleigh; Shire Publications,
Princes Risborough, Bucks.

Kitchenware
Jo Marshall; 1975, Pitman, London

Town and Country Kitchens
1992, Bracken Books, London

Metalware

Cast Iron
Jacqueline Fearn; Shire
Publications, Princes Risborough,
Bucks

Cast Iron Decoration
E. and J. Robertson; 1976, Thames
and Hudson, London

Pewter
Charles Hull; Shire Publications,
Princes Risborough, Bucks

**Pewter, A Celebration of the Craft
1200-1700**
P. Hornsby and R. Homer; 1989,
Museum of London

Pewter of Great Britain
C. A. Peal; 1983, John Gifford,
London

Plastics

**Classic Plastics: from Bakelite to
High Tech**
Sylvia Katz; Thames and Hudson,
London

Early Plastics
Sylvia Katz; Shire Publications,
Princes Risborough, Bucks

Pottery and Porcelain

*This is such an enormous subject that a
list could go on for the whole section.
These are only a selected few titles on
those subjects which might interest the
new collector.*

General:
**Bergesen's Price Guide
British Ceramics**
Victoria Bergesen, 1993, Barrie and
Jenkins, London
*Ms Bergesen gives an excellent
bibliography of individual and
specialised books which anyone
interested in the work of the last
century should have.*

**British 20th Century Studio
Ceramics**
Ian Bennett; 1980, Chistopher
Wood Gallery

**Handbook of Pottery and
Porcelain Marks**
John Cushion; Fourth Edition 1980,
Faber and Faber, London
*The most comprehensive and easy to
use marks book available now*

Illustrated Dictionary of Ceramics
George Savage and Harold
Newman; 1974, Thames and
Hudson, London

**Illustrated Guide to British
Pottery**
and
**Illustrated Guide to British
Porcelain**
Geoffrey Godden; 1974, Barrie and
Jenkins, London

All of Godden's books are classics and too numerous to mention. Beginners might start with his **Concise Guide to British Pottery and Porcelain**, 1990, Barrie and Jenkins, London.

Specialised:
Art Deco Tableware
Judy Spours; 1988, Ward Lock, London

British Studio Pottery
Oliver Watson; 1990, Phaidon Christie, Oxford

Collecting Pot Lids
Edward Fletcher; 1975, Pitman, London

Collecting Victorian Tiles
Terence Lockett; 1979, Antique Collectors' Club, Woodbridge Suffolk

Potters and Paintresses: Women Designers in the Pottery Industry 1870-1955
Cheryl Buckley; 1990, The Women's Press, London

The SylvaC Companion
Susan Verbeek; 1991, Pottery Publications

Tiles; A Collector's Guide
Hans van Lemmen; 1990, Souvenir Press, London

Victorian Art Pottery
E. Lloyd Thomas; 1974, Guildart

Prints and Etchings
How to Identify Old Prints
F. Wilder; 1969, Bell & Sons, London

The Flowering of Art Nouveau Graphics
Julia King; 1990, Trefoil Publications, London

The Japanese Print Since 1900
Lawrence Smith; 1983, British Museum Publications, London

Scent Bottles
Scent Bottles
Kate Foster; 1966, The Connoisseur, London

Scent Bottles
Alexandra Walker; Shire Publications, Princes Risborough, Bucks

Silver
Another huge subject so these are only a few suggestions.

Handbook to Hallmarks on Gold and Silver Plate
Chaffers; 1966, A. & C. Black

Silver
Banister; 1980 Macdonald, London

Silver for Pleasure and Investment
Geoffrey Wills; 1970, Crown, New York

Victorian Silver and Silver Plate
P. Wardle; 1963, Studio Vista, London

Major Markets and Fairs

This is a list of the major markets and fairs in Great Britain which occur regularly at the weekends.

Do remember that many of these are subject to cancellations and variation in opening times according to circumstances and local conditions. With few exceptions we have given telephone numbers for the organisers so that you can check on the latest information before you go.

Opening hours are as we have been given them, but please remember that almost all fairs open for trade visitors an hour earlier than scheduled. Admission at that time is usually by card, although some closed markets are more insistent on this than the open or outdoor markets, which have no restrictions.

There are many more fairs which are scheduled for mid-week, or for once-monthly appearances, etc.

For up-to-date information and complete local listings, please check your local paper or read the following weekly and monthly publications:
Antiques Traders Gazette
(weekly)
The Antique Trade Calendar
(bi-monthly)
The Collectors Calendar
(bi-monthly)

Many specialist magazines also list the exhibits and major fairs of that month or period. Throughout Great Britain there are smaller local fairs, markets and especially car boot sales now with amazing frequency. Learn to keep an eye out for card signs tacked up along main roads every weekend.

REGULAR FRIDAY EVENTS

LONDON
Bermondsey Antiques Market
Corner of Long Lane and Bermondsey Street, SE1
071 351 5353   Starts 5 am and is over by 2 pm. Huge, over 200 stalls. There are numerous surrounding Antiques Centres which are also open during the market as well as at normal hours during the week.

CHESHIRE
Collector's Market and Table Top Fair
Congleton Market Centre, Congleton
0477 537118
Up to 72 stalls   9am - 4pm

CUMBRIA
Antique and Collector's Fair
The Royal Hotel, Bowness-on-Windemere
0274 566196
Also every Thursday and Saturday
10am - 5pm

DORSET
Antiques Bazaar
Wimborne Market, Riverside Park Industrial Estate, Wimborne Minster
0202 841212 or 0860 844292
Up to 60 stalls 6am - 2:30pm

KENT
West Wickham Bric-a-brac Market
St Francis Church Hall, Ravenswood Avenue. West Wickham
081 686 0768
Up to 25 stalls 9am - 1pm

KENT
Fleamarket
The Angel Centre, Tonbridge
0732 456196
30 stalls 8am - 1pm

NORTHAMPTONSHIRE
Variety Market of Antiques, Bric-a-brac, Linen, Lace, etc.
Town Hall, Towcester
0908 225579
25 stalls 9am - 3pm

WARWICKSHIRE
Fleamarket
United Reformed Church, Chapel
Street, Nuneaton
0827 895899
Average 20 stalls 9:30am - 4pm

NORTH YORKSHIRE
Antique and Collector's Fair
Central Buildings, Market Square,
Leyburn
0969 663463
10am - 5pm

REGULAR SATURDAY EVENTS

LONDON
Portobello Road Antiques Market
Portobello Road, W11
Literally hundreds of shops and
stalls all along the street. 7am - 4pm,
although some stands start earlier
and many shops open later

Camden Passage Saturday Market
The Angel, Islington, N1
No telephone Includes shops as well
as stalls. 8am - 3pm for stalls; shops
normal Saturday opening

London Militaria Market
The Angel Arcade, 116-118 Islington
High Street, Camden Passage, N1
0628 822503
35 stalls 8am - 2pm

Antiques Market
The Stables, Chalk Farm Road,
Camden Town, NW1
Busy general market with crafts,
clothes, etc. Not primarily antiques.
Also on Sundays.
9am - 6pm, but many stalls don't
open until 10am or even later

Collector's Fair Market
London Bridge Station concourse
081 398 8065
50 stalls 8am - 3:30pm

Collector's Market
Bosuns Yard, 59 Greenwich Church
Street, Greenwich, SE10
081 293 4804
40 stalls 9:30 - 6:30 Also open

Major Markets and Fairs

Sundays and Bank Holiday
Mondays

Collector's Market
Charing Cross, junction of
Northumberland Ave and
Embankment Place WC2
081 398 8065
50 stalls 8am - 3:30 pm

CUMBRIA
Antique and Bygone Fair
St John's Hall, Ambleside
07687 76612
10am - 5pm Also open Sundays

NORFOLK
Craft Market
The Cloisters, St Andrews and
Blackfriars Halls, St Andrews Plain,
Norwich
10 am - 5pm

WEST SUSSEX
Arundel Antiques Market
At the River on River Road, Arundel
0243 582118
8am - 5pm

Treasure House Antiques Market
Crown Lane, behind Treasure
House, 31 High Street, Arundel
0903 507446
9am - 5pm

WEST YORKSHIRE
Fleamarket
Station Road, Sowerby Bridge
0422 359034
8am - 4pm

REGULAR SUNDAY EVENTS

LONDON

**See Saturday entry for Antiques
Market at the Stables, Chalk Farm**

**See Saturday entry for Collector's
Market at Bosuns Yard, Greenwich**

BIRMINGHAM
Antiques and Collector's Market
Holliday Wharf Antiques Centre
Holliday Street, Birmingham
021 643 9900
400 outdoor stands 9am - 5pm

BUCKINGHAMSHIRE
Antique and Collector's Fair
Wendover Antiques Centre, The Old
Post Office, Wendover
0296 625335
30 stalls 11am - 5:30pm

CUMBRIA
See Saturday entry for St John's Hall,
Ambleside

LANCASHIRE
Antique and Collector's Fair
Exhibition Halls, Park Hall,
Charnock Richard, near Chorley
061 773 7001
300 stalls 8:30am - 4pm

Collector's Market
The New Clitheroe Auction Mart
Clitheroe, off A59.
0253 782828
500 stalls, 8am - 4pm

Antique and Collector's Fair
Lancaster Leisure Park, Wyresdale
Road, Lancaster
0524 844734
Over 100 dealers 10am - 5pm
Open all Bank Holidays

GREATER MANCHESTER
Antique and Collector's Fair
Penny Farthing Street, Last Drop
Village, Bromley Cross, Bolton
0204 302395
35-40 stalls 11am - 4pm

WEST YORKSHIRE
Antique and Collector's Fair
Community Centre, Hebden Bridge,
near Halifax
0282 30670
30 stalls   10am - 5pm Open Bank
Holidays

So You Want to be a Dealer

Once you've been bitten by the collecting bug, and can't pass a shop or a stall without a browse, your home will become a growing showcase for the things you buy.

Gradually, as you build up a reasonable collection in your chosen subject, you begin to winnow out some of the worst mistakes or pieces which were once unusual to you but which you now realise are too commonplace for your liking.

Most collectors develop a working relationship with one or two dealers when they buy, and these down-graded pieces become part of an unofficial trade-in for something better or newer. And almost without knowing it, you're buying and selling at the same time. Then it seems logical to take the next step and become a dealer yourself.

If you are serious you should first consider all the pros and cons just as you would with any other business. Dealing in antiques, however fascinating and exciting and full of interest, is still a business with all the troubles and possibilities and paperwork that that entails. If you can't make it work on a professional basis, then the costs will outweigh the benefits by a very large margin.

Here are some of the points you should be thinking about.

Perhaps the first requirement will surprise you; assuming you begin as most of us do by taking a stall in a market rather than renting a shop, then above all you need stamina.

Look at the opening hours in our list of weekly markets. Most open between 8 and 9am, and they will have already been open for at least an hour before that for trade visitors. To be ready to deal at 7 or 7:30am means arriving around 6:30am, carrying all your things in and being ready to unpack and lay everything out as attractively as possible. Labelled, of course, with prices and a little information for your customers.

Then you must sit all day, with only a few breaks if you can arrange it, and then pack up only after closing hours before carrying a lot of it home again. And this on a Sunday or Bank Holiday Monday when everyone else is relaxing.

If the thought of this doesn't discourage you, then look at the finances. You will have to pay rent for your stall, which varies from place to place, but an average would be about £22-25 a day. Outdoors at a car boot sale it may only be £6 or £7, but you have to provide all the facilities including a table (a wall-papering table is ideal).

In an indoor market, you will get the table and usually electrical connections to each place so you can show off your goods with a lamp. But you must provide a cloth, and any extra stands to help the display look attractive. Many dealers collect little shelves and stands for their stall, and replace them as they sell them. A flat table-top is not very inviting to the customer.

I'd recommend finding a friend to share with, at least to start off and until you get to know your fellow dealers. You must look after the stall all the time, not only because of chance customers but because there is a certain amount of pilfering, and the bigger the fair the more there is.

You will have to put in a considerable amount of time in cleaning and tidying up what you buy, identifying it as correctly as possible, and setting a price. Be prepared to give a discount to the trade, and for some haggling from the customers, too. The most common failing of new dealers is to set their prices too low, pleasing themselves as a buyer rather than as a seller! But you must make each piece help to cover the costs, your time, and the effort and money it took to go out looking for enough stock. Equally, it doesn't make sense to try and charge more than something is likely to bring, just because you haven't sold enough that week. So it's a question of weighing up the various factors and coming up with reasonable prices that still leave you enough of a profit to cover your costs.

And making records of all of this. Doing the paperwork of what you buy, where from, what you pay and then what you receive may be boring and petty, but its absolutely vital for your tax returns as well as your own recognition of whether you are doing well or badly. You did want to be a dealer!

Index

Note: Page numbers in **bold type** refer to main sections on the subject listed. Page numbers in *italic type* refer to the glossary.

kitchen chairs 41, 43
kitchen, doll's 68, 69
kitchenware **96-101**
Kleister, J. 153
knife rests 166, 167
knife, fork and spoon set,
     child's 21
knives 62
   bread 63
knitting needle cases 156
knockers 34, 35
knop *189*
Kodak 36, 37

labels
   bottle 29
   enamelled tea 48
   wine 180, 181
lacquer 34, 48
lacquer boxes 14
ladies' razor 89
Lalique 154
Lambeth 139
lamps 34, 102, **104-5**, 115
   oil 119
lampwork *189*
Lane, Kenneth 60
latticinio *189*
laundry **106**
Leach, Bernard 142
lead 114
lead glass 78, 79
Leica 37
lemon squeezers 15, 100, 101
Leprince 150
letter boxes 33
letter lock 110
letter opener 91
letter racks 32, 161
letter scales 33
liberty pins 56

Liberty's 171
lids, pot 139
light, reading 34
lighter 57
lighting 102-5
Limerick 169
linen **106-7**
liners 79
lino cuts 146
lion design 167
lithography 152-3
Lloyd Loom 42
Lloyds insurance 46
locality 10
lockets 95
locks **108-11**, *192*
Loetz 82
Lorraine 173
Luckenbooth brooches 54
lunch hampers 23
lustre wares *189*

Macbeth, Anne 72, 107
Machin 111
Macintosh, Charles Rennie 40
magnifying glass 115
mahogany 175
Majolica 138, *191*
makers' marks 164
Malachite 24, 25
Manchester 76
manicure sets 89, 131
marble 76
markets 10, 12-13, *listed* 200-203
marks 62, 160, 164, 166
Martin brothers 142
Martini, I. 150
Mason's Ironstone 138, 139
match cases 166, 167
mauchline ware 169
measures, agricultural 183

My
GASTRONOMY

Nico Ladenis

"The cookery book of the year" *A la Carte*

"Nico Ladenis is an inspiration to our profession"
Anton Mosimann

"A loveable genius who creates transcendental meals"
Richard Olney

"A master of his craft" Katie Stewart

Nico Ladenis, the bald, bearded Franco-Greek of passionate
opinions and volcanic temper is one of the most brilliant and
controversial chef/restaurateurs of today. His London
restaurant, *Simply Nico*, boasts 2 Michelin stars and is fully
booked weeks in advance.

Now, readers everywhere can share the Nico experience in his
first book, which combines exquisite and innovative recipes
with his own firm and outspoken opinions on food, customers
and cooking.

Full of pungent anecdote, savoury advice and lightly salted
philosophy it is truly "the crème de la crème" *New Statesman*.

NON-FICTION/FOOD AND WINE   0 7472 3153 2

JUST THE ONE

THE WIVES AND TIMES OF
JEFFREY BERNARD

G R A H A M   L O R D

'One of the most thoroughly researched biographical enquiries I have read. It's all here, booze, women, Norman Balon, horses, "No-knickers Joyce", booze, and finally fame of a sort a writer rarely achieves in his lifetime' Patrick Marnham, *The Oldie*

Jeffrey Bernard, the legendary Soho journalist and boozer who has been popping down to the pub for 'just the one' for forty years is the most unlikely hero of our times.

What other bottle-of-vodka-and-fifty-fags-a-day hack has also been a gigolo, navvy, fairground boxer, miner, stagehand, film editor and actor? Who else has been married four times, seduced 500 lovers (including several renowned actresses) – and also written a famous column for the *Spectator*, his 'suicide note in weekly instalments'? In the astonishingly successful stage play, *Jeffrey Bernard is Unwell*, his rackety life has been portrayed by Peter O'Toole, Tom Conti, James Bolam and Dennis Waterman.

Graham Lord – who has known Bernard well for many years – has written a biography that is fun, devastatingly frank and critical, yet unexpectedly touching. Jeffrey Bernard is indeed unique – just the one.

'I wanted it to be longer. I read it from cover to cover in one sitting and laughed out loud and often' Paul Pickering, *Sunday Times*

'A gripping and unsentimental biography...an astonishing achievement' Irma Kurtz, *Sunday Express*

NON-FICTION/BIOGRAPHY   0 7472 4286 0

Ginger my story

GINGER ROGERS

'A LIVING LEGEND' *SUNDAY TELEGRAPH*

'The revealing memories of one of the cinema screen's greatest legends' *Hello!*

Ginger Rogers is one of Hollywood's most enduring legends. As the exquisite film partner of Fred Astaire, she danced her way into the hearts of people all over the world, starring in such classic films as *Top Hat*. But she was also a serious dramatic actress, winning an Oscar for her performance in *Kitty Foyle* in 1940. Now, for the first time, Ginger tells her story.

Ginger talks of her legendary partnership with Fred Astaire which led to some of the most magical moments the screen has ever seen. She also tells the true, and, at times, sad story of her five marriages, and of her performing partners – Jimmy Stewart, Cary Grant, Henry Fonda, Katharine Hepburn.

Ginger Rogers' heart-warming and revealing memoirs paint a vivid portrait of a much-loved actress; and of a glittering Hollywood era, now vanished.

NON-FICTION/AUTOBIOGRAPHY   0 7472 3850 2

A selection of non-fiction from Headline

THE *INDEPENDENT* BOOK OF ANNIVERSARIES	George Beal	£8.99 ☐
MEAN BEANS	Cas Clarke	£5.99 ☐
ENCYCLOPEDIA OF FORENSIC SCIENCE	Brian Lane	£7.99 ☐
JUST THE ONE: The Wives and Times of Jeffrey Bernard	Graham Lord	£6.99 ☐
MALE SEXUAL AWARENESS	Barry McCarthy	£5.99 ☐
BURNS: A Biography of Robert Burns	James Mackay	£8.99 ☐
WORLD ENCYCLOPEDIA OF 20TH CENTURY MURDER	Jay Robert Nash	£8.99 ☐
PLAYFAIR FOOTBALL ANNUAL 1993-94	Jack Rollin (Ed)	£3.99 ☐
HEART AND SOLE	David Sole with Derek Douglas	£5.99 ☐

All Headline books are available at your local bookshop or newsagent, or can be ordered direct from the publisher. Just tick the titles you want and fill in the form below. Prices and availability subject to change without notice.

Headline Book Publishing PLC, Cash Sales Department, Bookpoint, 39 Milton Park, Abingdon, OXON, OX14 4TD, UK. If you have a credit card you may order by telephone – 0235 831700.

Please enclose a cheque or postal order made payable to Bookpoint Ltd to the value of the cover price and allow the following for postage and packing:
UK & BFPO: £1.00 for the first book, 50p for the second book and 30p for each additional book ordered up to a maximum charge of £3.00.
OVERSEAS & EIRE: £2.00 for the first book, £1.00 for the second book and 50p for each additional book.

Name ....

Address ....

....

....

If you would prefer to pay by credit card, please complete:
Please debit my Visa/Access/Diner's Card/American Express (delete as applicable) card no:

Signature .... Expiry Date ....